IMAGE COMICS
PRESENTS

SLEEP

WRITTEN AND DRAWN BY
ZANDER CANNON

PUBLICATION DESIGN BY
DYLAN TODD

IMAGE COMICS, INC. • Robert Kirkman: Chief Operations Officer • Erik Larsen: Chief Financial Officer • Todd McFarlane: President • Marc Silvestri: Chief Executive Officer • Jim Valentino: Vice President • Eric Stephenson: Publisher & Chief Creative Officer • IMAGECOMICS.COM

SLEEP. First printing. June 2026. Published by Image Comics, Inc. Office of publication: PO BOX 14457, Portland, OR 97293.

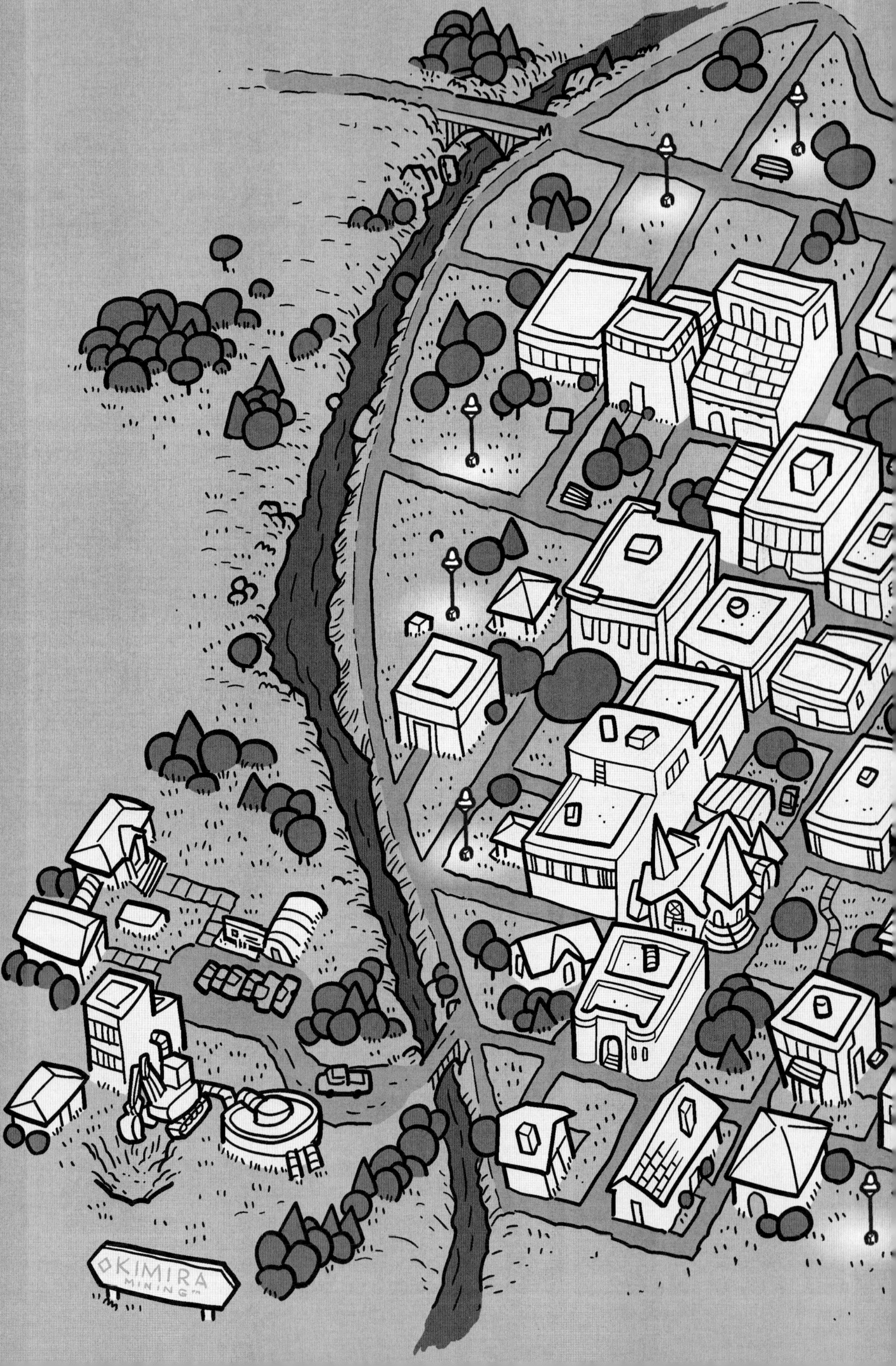
KIMIRA
MINING™

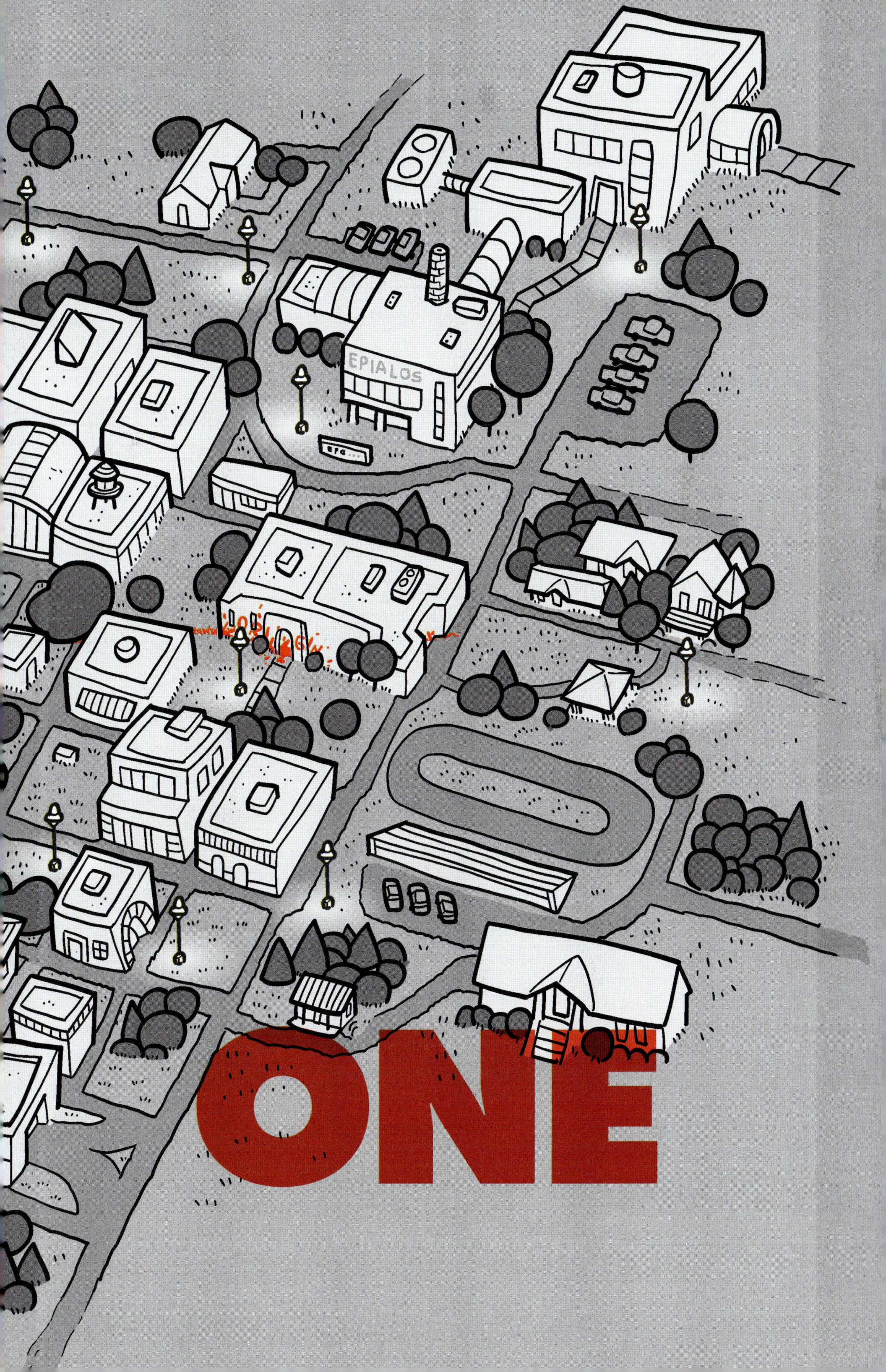

ONE

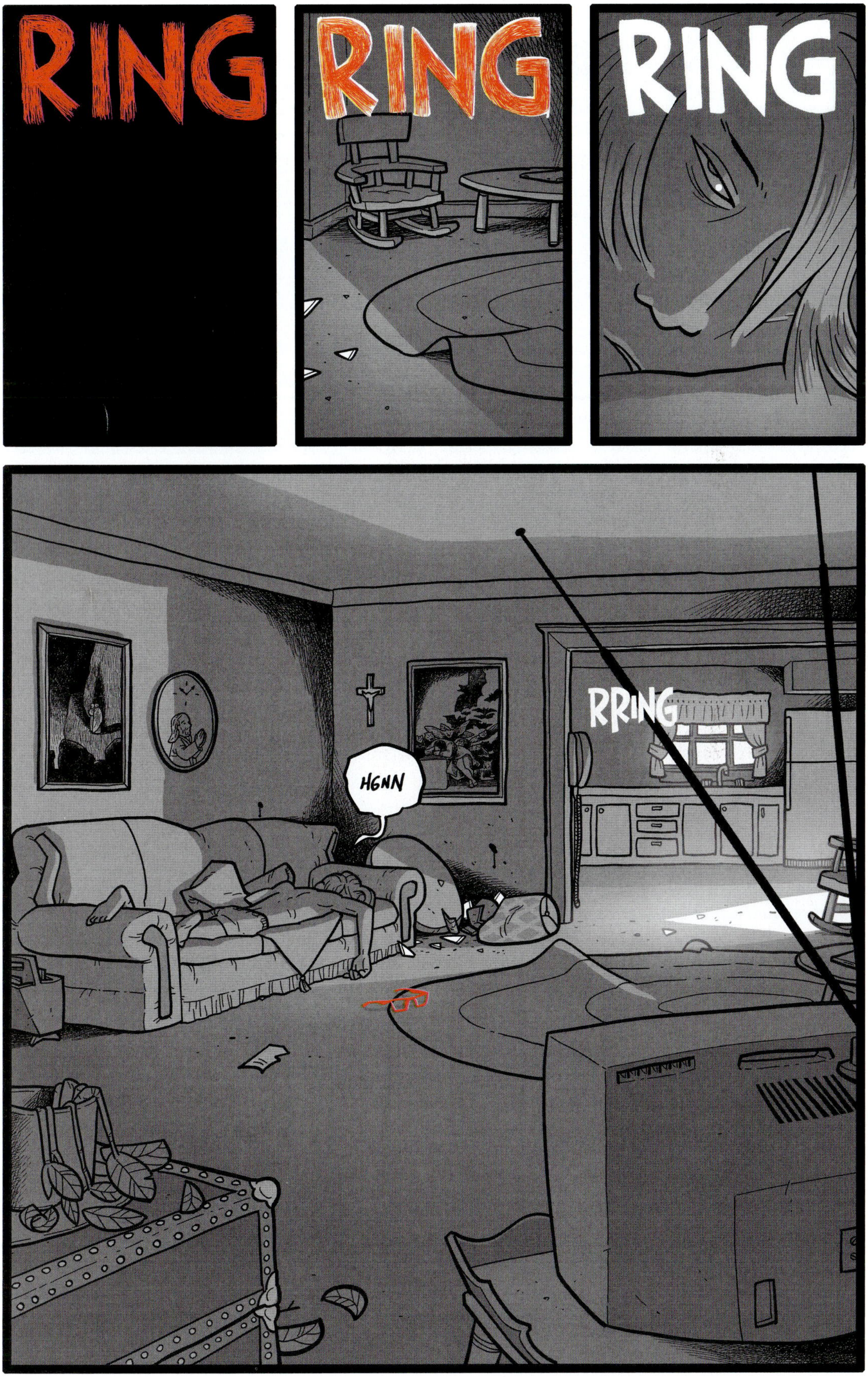
RING
RING
RING
RRING
HGNN

KCHAK
HELLO?
JONATHAN? YOU OKAY? IT'S TABBY.
HEY. YEAH, I'M OKAY, WHY?
WE WERE SUPPOSED TO MEET FOR COFFEE BEFORE CHURCH. BUT--
Ecch. Ah, MAN...
WHAT TIME IS--
Ah JEEZ.
IT'S LATE.
Uh, YEAH IT IS!
AND WITH THE STUFF THAT WENT DOWN LAST NIGHT, I WAS WORRIED!
WHY, WHAT HAPPENED LAST NIGHT?
SCOOP
WH-LIKE... I-- CRAZY STUFF. DIDN'T YOU HEAR ANY OF IT?
RATTLE
NO, I-I GUESS I WAS SLEEPING REALLY SOUND--
Ah, HECK.
WHAT?
Oh, I THINK THE CAT GOT OUT. THE DOOR'S OPEN.
I'LL FIND HIM LATER.
LISTEN, TAB, I'M SORRY I'M LATE. I'LL MEET YOU THERE IN JUST A FEW MINUTES.

NO! NO, YOU GOT TO FIND HIM NOW.
WHAT? WHY?
EEEE
'CAUSE, LIKE, THERE'S SOMETHING OUT THERE, JONATHAN!
LIKE A WILD ANIMAL, THEY'RE SAYING.
EEEEE
I GUESS IT KILLED A BUNCH OF COWS...?
IT WASN'T THAT FAR FROM YOUR HOUSE.
EEEEEEEE
LIKE, I DON'T KNOW HOW YOU DIDN'T HEAR IT.
JONATHAN?
MITTENS
EEEEEEEEEEE
JON?
EEEE--

SUNDAY

VIRTUE, LADIES AND GENTLEMEN.
AND SIN.
THAT'S WHAT WE'RE ADDRESSING TODAY.
HEY.
HEY! DID YOU FIND HER?
NO, I LOOKED AND LOOKED, BUT...
I MEAN, CATS HIDE. I'M SURE SHE'S SOMEPLACE.
TOTALLY. LIKE, SHE'LL SHOW UP.
IT'S JUST THAT WHEN MY MOM WAS ALIVE, MITTENS WAS HERS. Y'KNOW?
AND TABBY, MY HOUSE. SOMETHING WEIRD IS--
DO YOU KIDS MIND?
BE QUIET.
AND FIND US, WHEREVER WE ARE.
WORLDLINESS, SECULARITY, AND LUST.
THEY'VE LED TO THE DOWNFALL OF GOOD PEOPLE EVEN IN THIS TOWN, RARE AS IT IS.
I MEAN, WE ALL KNOW OF JEREMIAH LAWSON.
"KIDS."
I SAID SHH!
BUT LIFE IN THE CITY? WELL, FRIENDS, IT SEES DECADENCE ON A SCALE UNKNOWN TO US.
HERE TO TALK -- haha, OR RATHER SING -- ABOUT BOTH HIS EXPERIENCES THERE AND HIS SALVATION...

PLEASE WELCOME OUR OWN NATIVE SON, WHO HAS COME TO THIS CHURCH SINCE HE WAS JUST A LITTLE GUY...
HIPPOCRATES NICOLI!
THE ENEMY AT THE GATE
WHAT? Oh WOW.
CRAZY.
TAB, THAT'S HIPP. HE AND I WENT TO...
...SCHOOL TOGETHER...
THANKS, PASTOR STEPHEN.
IT'S BEEN A LONG TIME.
THIS IS A SONG ABOUT SIN.

AND I HOPE MY WORDS FIND THE PEOPLE THEY'RE MEANT TO.
STRUM
THIS WORLD, SO FALLEN
AND THE DEVIL, HE'S CALLIN'
THE INFERNAL SIGNS, THE BELLS ARE RUNG
THE CONSEQUENCE CAN'T BE UNDONE
RICH OR POOR, SIN'S BLOODY TRAIL
JUDGMENT COMES, IF YOU SUCCEED OR FAIL.
MY BROTHERS.
TUMP
WE MUST STAND STRONG ATOP THAT WALL.
THE SIN
THE FATE
DESTROYS
THE GATE
WORLD OF TEMPTATION
THOUSAND WAYS TO FALL
GIVE THE DEVIL ONE MAN
HE'LL TAKE THEM ALL
AMEN.
CLAP CLAP CLAP CLAP CLAP CLAP CLAP CLAP CLAP
THANK YOU. THANK YOU VERY MUCH.

HEYYY!
HE'S BACK!
THAT'S RIGHT, THE PRODIGAL SON IS IN THE HOUSE.
PLEASE FORM AN ORDERLY LINE TO KISS MY ASS.
AND YOU GO FIRST.
Ha ha!
HOW ARE YOU, DUDE?
I'M ALL RIGHT.
COMING BACK TO A TOWN WITH ONE STOPLIGHT'S A DOWNGRADE, I WON'T LIE TO YOU.
BUT SHIT GOT REAL SIDEWAYS WITH THE BAND I WAS IN, SO I'M HERE FOR A LITTLE WHILE.
DON'T SUPPOSE YOU KNOW ANY OTHER GIGS BESIDES THE ONE WITH A SERMON AS THE WARMUP ACT?
heh.
NOT OFF THE TOP OF MY HEAD.
BUT-BUT FIRST THINGS FIRST...
THIS IS TABBY. TABITHA.
HI.
SHE WORKS OVER AT THE LAB AT EPG.
OH YEAH? DOING WHAT?
Uh, BIOMEDICAL RESEARCH.
Ah, COLLEGE GIRL, huh?
NO WONDER HE LIKES YOU.
IS THAT RIGHT?

HOW COME HE KEEPS TELLING ME I'M **SELLING OUT**, THEN?
Oh MY GOD, **STILL**?
HE'S ALWAYS BEEN THIS WAY. **MR. PURE** OVER HERE.
I USED TO BE ON BOARD, BUT A DOSE OF THE REAL WORLD CURES YOU OF THAT STUFF **REAL** QUICK.
SO D'YOU TELL HIM HE NEEDS TO JOIN THE PEACE CORPS OR **SHUT UP**?
Ha ha! I **SHOULD**!
HIPP! THANK YOU **SO MUCH** FOR COMING.
IT'S NICE TO HAVE YOU BACK IN TOWN-- A REMINDER OF THE GOOD OLD DAYS, eh?
DO YOU HAVE A MOMENT?
SERMON - STEPHEN
SURE, OF COURSE, PASTOR STEPHEN.
SAY, WAY BACK, YOUR DAD HUNG THAT CROSS UP IN THE CHAPEL FOR US.
IT'S GETTING A LITTLE LOOSE, AND I KNOW HE'S BUSY WITH EVERYTHING, BUT MAYBE IF **YOU'VE** GOT SOME TIME...?
HEY, TABBY, I GOTTA **GO**. I HAVE TO BE THERE AT ONE.
RIGHT, RIGHT. OKAY. I'LL COME BY AND SAY HI LATER.
SO, I GUESS I **DO** HAVE A GIG, SAD AS IT--
HEY, YOU LEAVING?
Ah, YEAH, I GOTTA WORK. THE **COFFEE SHOP** OVER ON **PARK**.
I MIGHT HAVE KNOWN.
HUNDRED PERCENT ON BRAND FOR YOU.
STEPHEN
3:00
5:00
THANK **GOD** NEITHER ONE OF US IS SELLING OUT.
TODAY, ANYWAY.

TOKTOK
KTUNK
TSSSHH
HOT DRINKS
LATTE 1.80 2.09
BREAKFAST
COLD DRINKS
DESSERTS
TRIVIA
WHAT IS THE
NAME OF THE
KRSHT
QUI VIVE
TIPS

BA-DING
HELLO, HELLO!
THE BOSS ISN'T HERE TODAY?
Oh, uh, SHE AND HER DAUGHTER ARE JUST OUT GETTING SOME LUNCH.
WHAT CAN I GET YOU, MR. EDISON?
Ah ha ha. JUST A REGULAR CUP OF COFFEE.
NONE OF THAT WEIRD STUFF.
June 6 19 96
2468
1.33
CHECK OKAY?
SURE. HERE YOU GO.
QUI VIVE
WHAT'S UP, TURBO?
HI, DYLAN.
OFFICER BRYSON. LATTE. EXTRA FOAM.
Uh... OKAY. I MEAN, THAT'S MORE OF A CAPPU--
YEAH. COMING RIGHT UP.
QUI VIVE
BA-DING

HEY, MYRNA, HOW WAS IT?
OH BOY. KELLY HAD US GO TO THIS NEW "FUSION" PLACE.
BIG MISTAKE.
I DON'T KNOW WHY EVERY NEW RESTAURANT HAS TO BE SO "EDGY" THESE DAYS.
WEIRD FOOD? SWEAR WORDS ON THE MENU? MEAN WAITERS? HONESTLY.
QUI VIVE
I'M PUTTING THE "LEFTOVERS" IN THE BACK ROOM IF YOU'RE INTERESTED.
Oh, AND KELLY SAYS SHE CAN'T OPEN TOMORROW.
I--
WELL--
SOMETHING WITH HER FRIENDS.
ANYWAY. I NEED YOU TO DO IT. SIX A.M.
I--uh, OKAY, SURE, IF YOU NEED ME TO.
KRSHHTT
SIX A.M. GOT IT.
HERE YOU GO, OFFICER BRYSON.
THANKS, TURBO.
BADING
Oh, NO WAY.

YOU'RE A COP NOW? WHO THE HELL MADE THAT DECISION?
Ha ha!
MAYBE YOU SHOULD TALK TO YOUR DAD ONCE IN A WHILE, PUNK.
NOT IF I CAN HELP IT.
HELL ARE YOU?
HI.
HI.
SO, ah...
YOUR FRIEND'S PRETTY FUNNY.
ALL RIGHT, PLAYER. THINGS ARE NUTS. I GOT TO GET BACK TO IT.
COOL. I'LL SWING BY THE STATION IF MY DAD'S NOT AROUND.
PEACE.
CLOSED
SO DYL-WEED IS THE LAW IN THIS TOWN, huh?
JESUS, AND I THOUGHT IT WAS BAD BEFORE.
I GUESS SMOKING POT BEHIND THE BLEACHERS DOES HAVE A FUTURE.
tsk
Oh. HEY, MISS MILLER.
HIPP.
INTERESTING TO SEE YOU BACK IN TOWN.

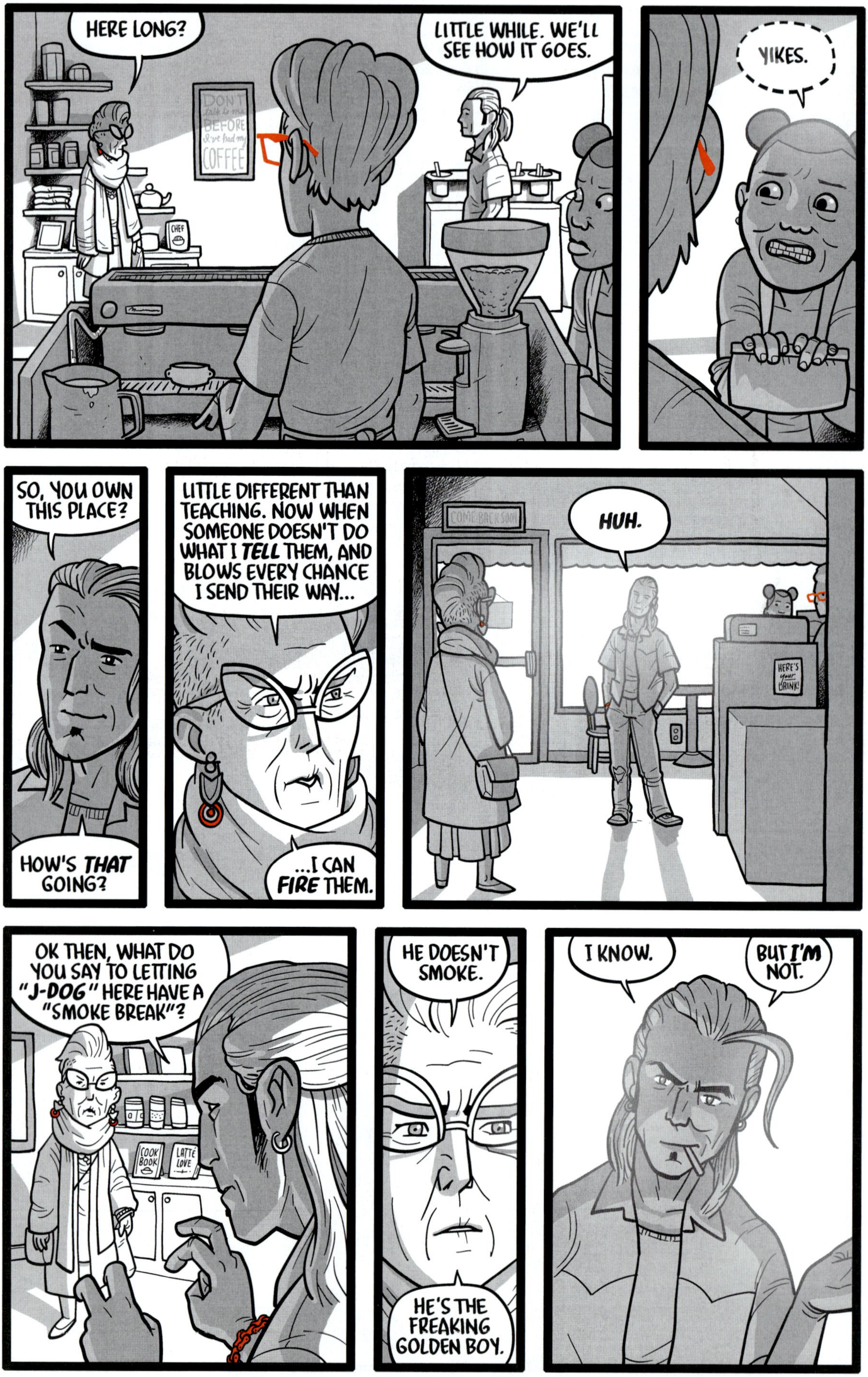
HERE LONG?
DON'T talk to me BEFORE I've had my COFFEE
CHEF
LITTLE WHILE. WE'LL SEE HOW IT GOES.
YIKES.
SO, YOU OWN THIS PLACE?
HOW'S THAT GOING?
LITTLE DIFFERENT THAN TEACHING. NOW WHEN SOMEONE DOESN'T DO WHAT I TELL THEM, AND BLOWS EVERY CHANCE I SEND THEIR WAY...
...I CAN FIRE THEM.
COME BACK SOON
HUH.
HERE'S your DRINK!
OK THEN, WHAT DO YOU SAY TO LETTING "J-DOG" HERE HAVE A "SMOKE BREAK"?
COOK BOOK
LATTE LOVE
HE DOESN'T SMOKE.
HE'S THE FREAKING GOLDEN BOY.
I KNOW.
BUT I'M NOT.

SO HE COMES TEARING OUT PAST THE SHACK AT 3 A.M., SIREN GOING, EVERYTHING.
PISSED AS **HELL**.
I'M SURE THE TERRIFIED FARMER ON THE SCENE GOT A **REAL** QUALITY INVESTIGATION.
BOTH OF THEM KNEE-DEEP IN GUTS, MY DAD JUST YELLING AT HIM TO CHILL OUT. I **LOVE** IT.
SO, WHAT WAS IT? DID THEY FIGURE IT OUT?
tsk
WHO KNOWS. WOLF, PROBABLY?
WELL...
WHATEVER IT WAS, I THINK IT NEARLY **MURDERED** ME LAST NIGHT.

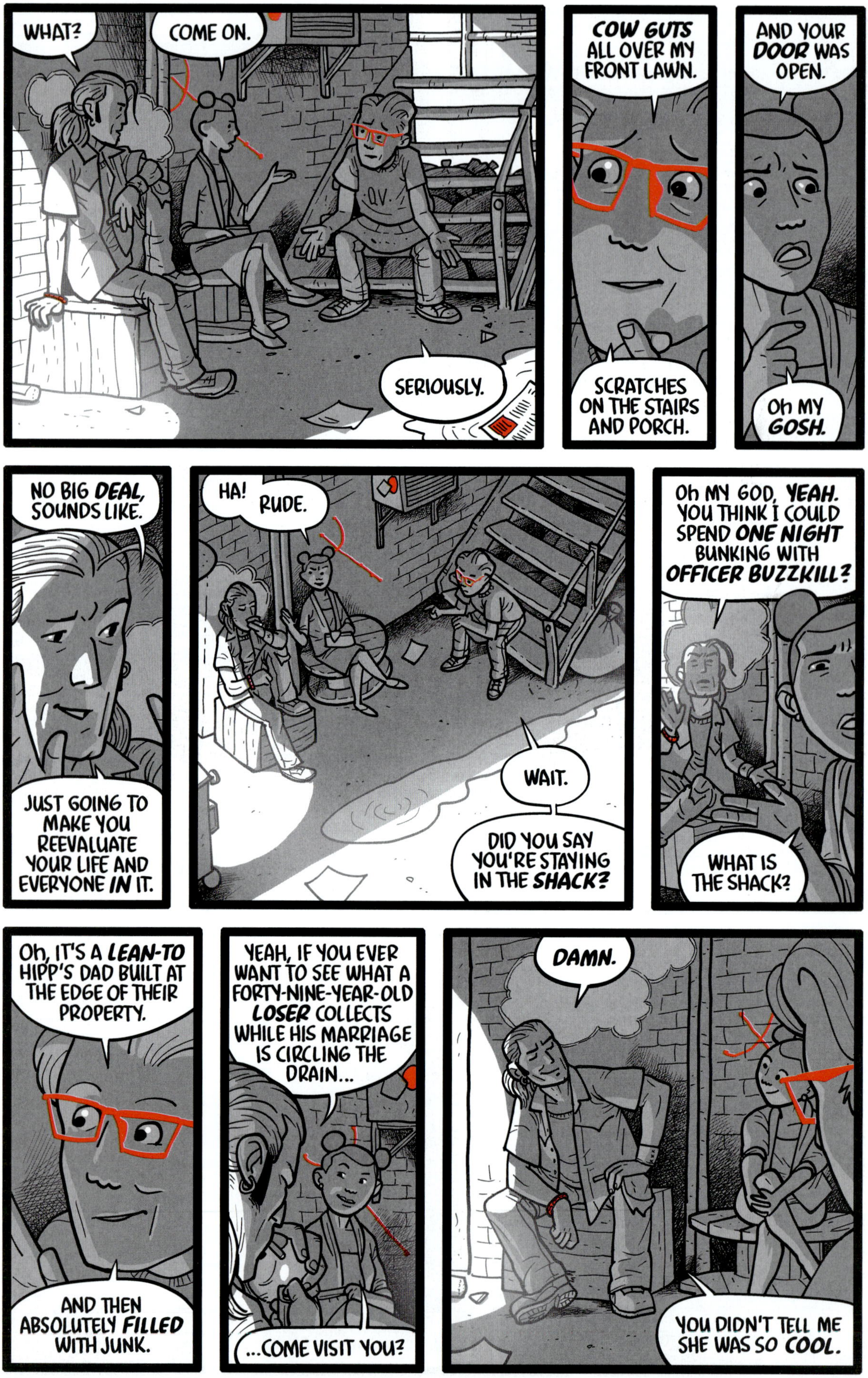
WHAT?
COME ON.
SERIOUSLY.
COW GUTS ALL OVER MY FRONT LAWN.
SCRATCHES ON THE STAIRS AND PORCH.
AND YOUR DOOR WAS OPEN.
Oh MY GOSH.
NO BIG DEAL, SOUNDS LIKE.
JUST GOING TO MAKE YOU REEVALUATE YOUR LIFE AND EVERYONE IN IT.
HA!
RUDE.
WAIT.
DID YOU SAY YOU'RE STAYING IN THE SHACK?
Oh MY GOD, YEAH. YOU THINK I COULD SPEND ONE NIGHT BUNKING WITH OFFICER BUZZKILL?
WHAT IS THE SHACK?
Oh, IT'S A LEAN-TO HIPP'S DAD BUILT AT THE EDGE OF THEIR PROPERTY.
AND THEN ABSOLUTELY FILLED WITH JUNK.
YEAH, IF YOU EVER WANT TO SEE WHAT A FORTY-NINE-YEAR-OLD LOSER COLLECTS WHILE HIS MARRIAGE IS CIRCLING THE DRAIN...
...COME VISIT YOU?
DAMN.
YOU DIDN'T TELL ME SHE WAS SO COOL.

KROCK
FLIPFLIP
GZZZT
KCHIK
FRANCIS
B BANK
KLIK
COME BACK SOON
CLOSED
KLIK KLIK
CLOSED
FLIP
KCHAK
QV
SPARE SOME CHANGE?
Ah!
SORRY. I, uh...
YEAH.
I THINK I HAVE SOME.
ONE SEC.

HERE YOU GO, MRS. LAWSON.
DON'T.
DON'T YOU DARE.
D-DON'T YOU DARE CALL ME BY HIS FUCKING NAME.
DON'T YOU DARE CALL ME BY HIS FUCKING NAME!
SAV SUM
CLOSED
snf
SAV SUM

SHFF
SHFF
SH--
QUI-VIVE
BODY
GATE
Death
ACCOMPL
ORIGIN
PUNISHM

CARVER HIG
ARCANA
DRUGS
HOMECOMING
SPIRIT DAY +
GAME FRIDAY
DANCE SATURDAY
QUI VIVE
HEY, uh...
NEVER MIND.

MITTENS?
PSS PSS HERE, KITTY.

KLIK
sigh
...HOW THE...
angry elephant
SWEEP
CRASH
QV
CRINKLE

CRK
CRUNCH
YOU ARE THE CAUSE
OF YOUR OWN PROBLEM
CRNKL
pss pss pss
KCHK

MITTENS
END CHAPTER ONE

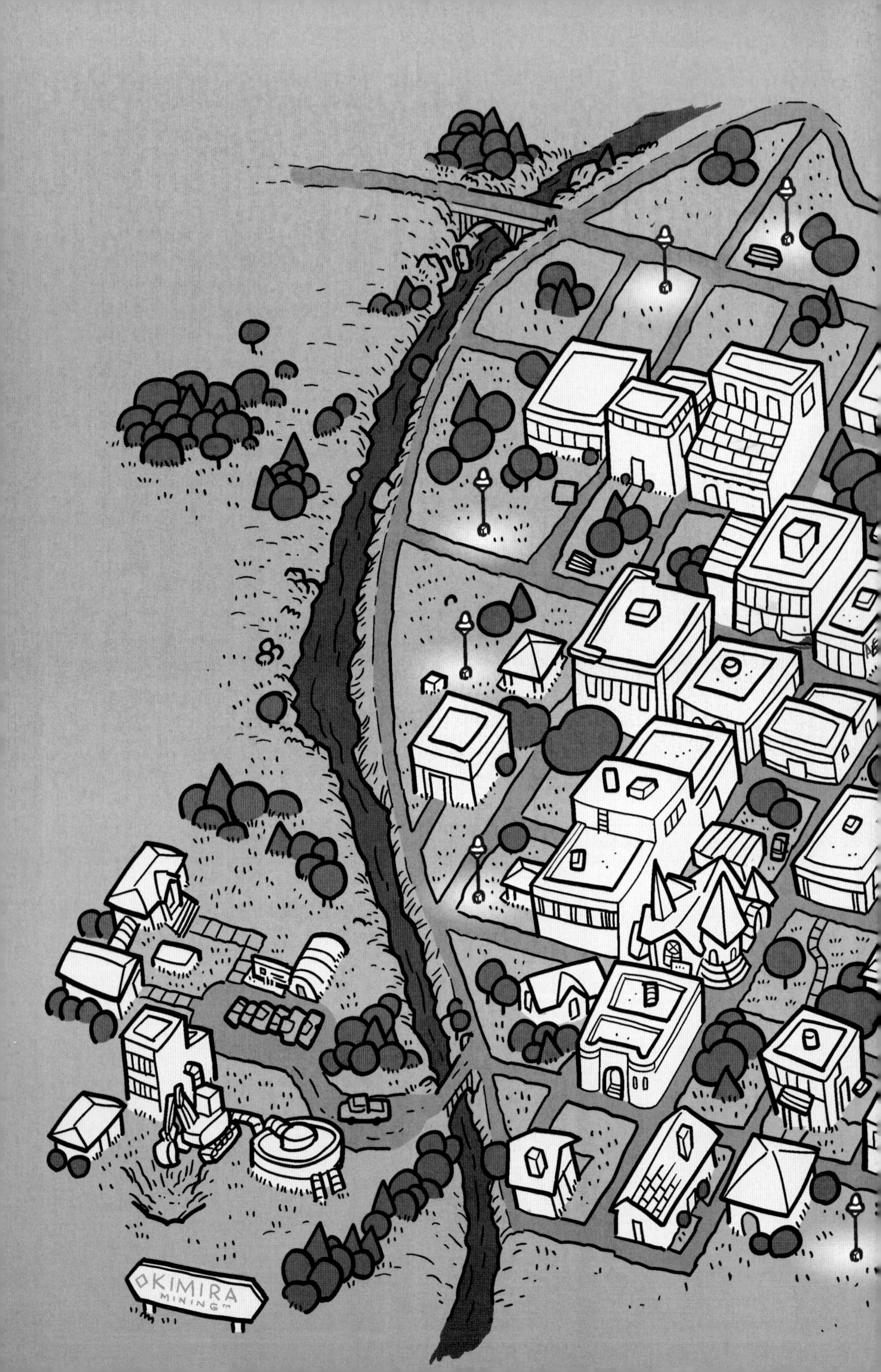
KIMIRA
MINING™

TWO

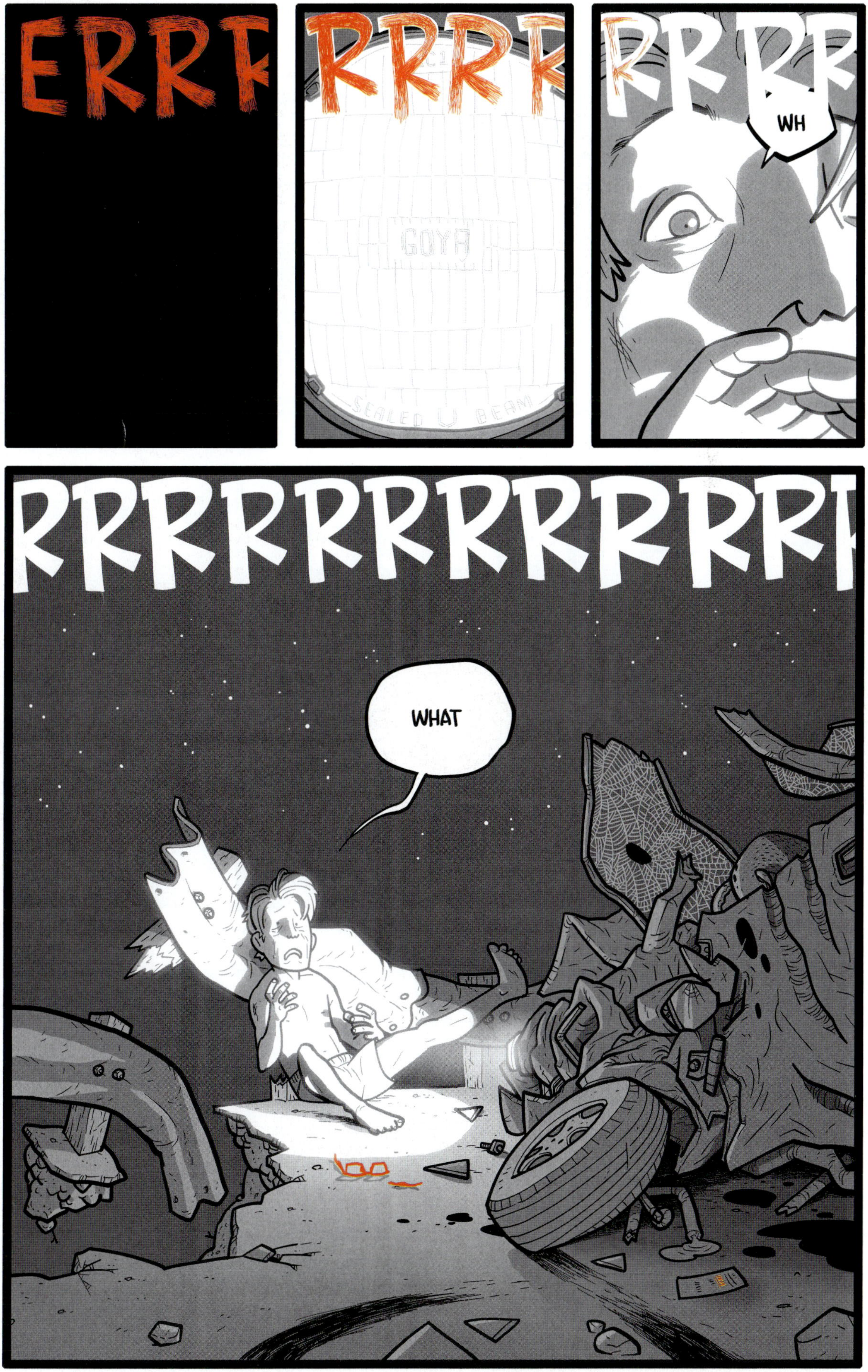
ERRR
RRRR
GOYA
SEALED BEAM
RRRR
WH
RRRRRRRRRRRRR
WHAT

WHAT
WHERE
RRRRRRRRR
RRRRRRRRRRRRRRRRR

P-PASTOR STEPHEN?
Oh MY GOD.
OHMY GODOH MY GOD
WH- WHAT IS HAPPEN-ING?
PLEASE, PASTOR STEPHEN, ARE YOU--
KOFF
JESUS!
SKTCH
KTANG
PAF
SPLASH

WHAT--WHAT IS HAPPENING?
WHAT IS HAPPENING?
nnf I DON'T UNDERSTAND.
GOD, WHAT IS--
OV HE
Oh GOD
JESUS
IS HE DEAD
THE COPS
WHO IS IT

BREATHING
PASTOR
HE HIT
SIRENS
WHAT IS
FROM THE
WHERE
LAST
AROUND
THE
THAT DAMN THING
GOTTA BE STOPPED
GOTTA KILL THAT THING
DEAR GOD
AROUND HERE SOMEWHERE, DON'T IT?
MY CAR
EEEEEE

IT'S GOTTA BE CLOSE BY
EEEEEEEE
EEE
EMERGENCY CALL 911 FIRE POLICE MED
KILL IT
MY GO
THANK GOD YOU'RE
OFFICER
THERE'S THE AMBULANCE
OKAY TAKE IT EASY TURBO
TOLD YOU
EEEOOO
A HUGE CRASH
THE BACK OF THE CAR
OUT LATE I GUESS
OKAY, EVERYONE, LET'S CLEAR OUT.
ME AND THE EMTs HAVE GOT THIS.
WE'LL FIND WHO'S RESPONSIBLE, OKAY?
SO ALL YOU FOLKS JUST GO ON...

MONDAY

JESUS
JESUS
THRIFT
DONATION
RUSTLE
SCRAPE
KCHIK
KLONK
SHFF
TIE TIE
CHFF
FLIP
OPEN

HI, SORRY. C'MON IN. SORRY.
COME BACK SOON
KLIK
QUI VIVE
LATE NIGHT, KID?
Haha. YEAH, I GUESS.
COUPLE CUPS OF COFFEE OUGHT TO SOBER YOU UP, huh?
C'MON, YOU EVER MET THIS KID BEFORE?
MY LITTLE SISTER WENT TO SCHOOL WITH HIM. HE'S A TOTAL GOODY TWO-SHOES.
Huh. GOODY ZERO-SHOES IS MORE LIKE IT. LARGE COFFEE.

TSSSH
CLINK
VRRN
KRSHT
THERE YOU GO.
THANKS.
COME BACK SOON
BA-DING
CLOSED

NO PERSONAL CALLS
BEEP BOOP BOOP BOOP
BRRRT BRRT
C'MON, C'MON...
KLIK YOU'VE REACHED TABIT... I'M NOT AT HO... RIGHT NOW, BU... ...YOU LEAVE YOUR ...ME AND NUMBER ...GET RIGHT BACK TO YOU.
Oh, COME ON.
BEEEP
T-TABBY, THIS IS JONATHAN. I-I GOTTA TALK TO YOU. THERE'S-- uh...
IT'S LIKE SEVEN THIRTY, WHERE ARE YOU? I'M GOING TO TRY YOU AT WORK.
BA-DING
Oh, FOR... BE RIGHT THERE!
I'LL TALK TO YOU LATER, TABBY.
OKAY, SORRY ABOUT THE WAIT. WHAT CAN I GET--
...YOU...
DON'T talk to me BEFORE I've had my COFFEE
NICOLI
Uh...
H-HI, CHIEF NICOLI.

WH--
WHAT CAN I GET YOU...?
WHOO
JESUS.
YOU GOT ANY WHISKEY?
Ah haha
T-TOUGH MORNING?
YEAH. JUST A COFFEE, PLEASE, JON.
IT'S A CRAZY ONE OUT THERE, MAYBE YOU KNOW.
YEAH, I-I, uh, I HEARD A BIG NOISE WH-WHEN I WAS OPENING.
WHAT'S--
CAR CRASH. CAN'T GO INTO DETAILS. EVERYTHING'S GOT TO RUN THROUGH THE SYSTEM.
GET 'EM TO THE HOSPITAL, NOTIFY FAMILY, ALL THAT.
PICK UP
COMPILE ALL THE EVIDENCE, Y'KNOW? THAT'S HOW THESE THINGS ARE SOLVED.
S-SOLVED?
YEAH. THERE'S ALL KINDS OF QUESTIONS. BUT I GOT ALL THESE COWBOYS WORKING FOR ME, AND THEY NEVER SEEM TO REMEMBER THAT THE DEVIL'S IN THE DETAILS.
SAY...
...WHAT HAPPENED TO YOUR GLASSES?
I-I, uh--
I B-BROKE THE--
THEY, uh, BROKE.
BA-DING

HEY. JON. GET OUTTA HERE.
YOU'RE RELIEVED.
COME BACK SOON
H-HI KELLY. THANKS.
ALL RIGHT THEN.
JON, YOU OUGHT TO RUN BY EDISON'S OPTICAL WHEN IT OPENS. I'VE KNOWN HIM A LONG TIME--HE CAN BE COUNTED ON.
YOU KIDS HAVE A GOOD ONE.
"KIDS."
OKAY, MY MOM SAID I GOTTA GET IN HERE AND TAKE OVER.
OOUGH..
YOU, ah, DOING OKAY?
HA!
YEAH, JUST HUNGOVER AS SHIT.
FOR ALL THE GOOD THE PIOUS LITTLE LECTURE WE GOT OUTSIDE THE LIQUOR STORE DID.
"AREN'T YOU GIRLS CONCERNED ABOUT YOUR VIRTUE?"

Uh, **NO**, PASTOR STEPHEN, I'M **NOT.**
QUI VIVE
QUI·VIVE
AND FURTHERMORE, MIND YOUR OWN **BUSINESS**, YOU UPTIGHT BITCH.
I TOLD HIM TO GO FIND SOME **REAL** EVIL TO FIGHT.
KELLY, DID YOU SAY **PASTOR STEPHEN?**
CLOSED
YEAH, WHY?
LET'S, uh...
I JUST WANT TO ASK YOU A FEW **QUESTIONS.**
WHAT? WHY?
QUI·VIVE
D ESTABLISH A
MELINE HERE...
TIMELINE FOR **WHAT?**
BA-DING
COMEBACK SOON
CLOSED

WHOO
QUI · VI
GET THAT PIECE
--DON'T KNOW IF YOU'LL SALVAGE ANYTHING OUT OF THIS ONE--
CAREFUL
OPTICAL
CAR

Oh, WATCH YOUR STEP THERE, YOUNG JONATHAN!
SORRY ABOUT THE MESS.
GUESS THERE WAS SOME KIND OF TO-DO IN THE NIGHT, eh?
AND YOUR LOCAL OPTICAL SHOP WAS IN THE WRONG PLACE AT THE WRONG TIME.
SPECIALS
HONESTLY, WHAT THIS SLEEPY OLD TOWN GETS UP TO I'LL NEVER KNOW.
Uh, Y-YEAH.
AH!
BROKEN GLASSES, hmm? LET ME SEE THOSE.
Oh, I CAN HAVE THIS SLAPPED BACK TOGETHER IN TWO MINUTES.
COME WITH ME.
Phone
A-ACTUALLY, MR. EDISON...
CAN I BORROW A QUARTER?
DRUG
KTING
US COINS ONLY
THE EPG GENERAL SWITCHBOARD. PLEASE ENTER THE THREE-DIGIT EXTEN--
BEEP BOOP BOOP
sniff
BRRT BRRT KLIK YOU'VE REACHED TABITHA STEVENS AT RESEARCH LAB FOUR. I'M NOT AT MY DESK AT THE MOMENT. IF THIS IS URGENT, PLEASE DIAL ZERO TO SPEAK TO AN OPER--
KLUNK
K-CHING

BA-DING
Ah! THERE YOU ARE.
ALMOST FINISHED.
JUST HAD TO POP A NEW SCREW IN THERE, AND...
BA-DING
Oh!
MORE CUSTOMERS!
HELLO, MAYA. NICE TO SEE YOU AGAIN.
THERE YOU GO, YOUNG MAN.
NO CHARGE.
NOW. I DON'T WANT TO KEEP YOU...

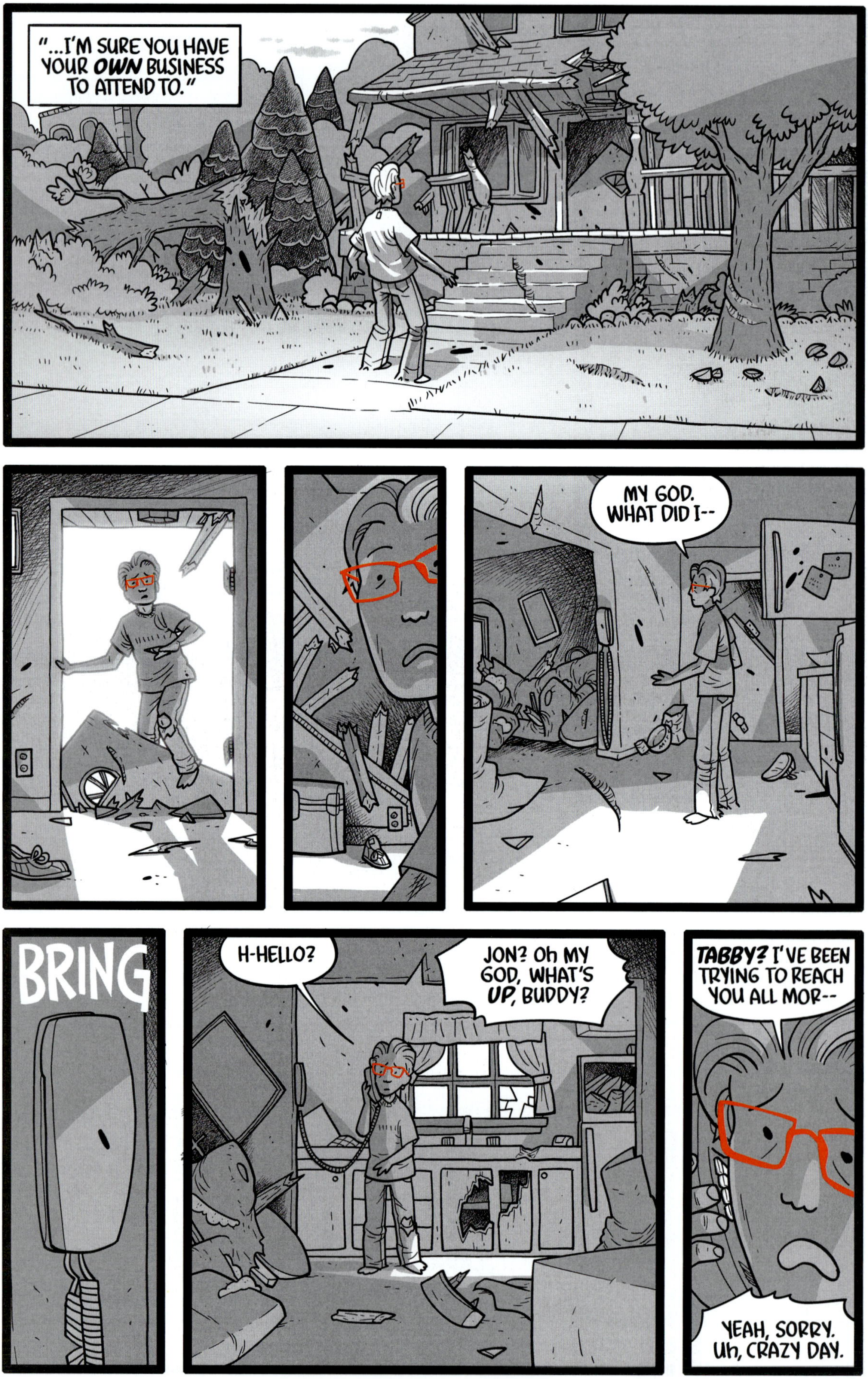
"...I'M SURE YOU HAVE YOUR OWN BUSINESS TO ATTEND TO."
MY GOD. WHAT DID I--
BRING
H-HELLO?
JON? Oh MY GOD, WHAT'S UP, BUDDY?
TABBY? I'VE BEEN TRYING TO REACH YOU ALL MOR--
YEAH, SORRY. Uh, CRAZY DAY.

A-ARE YOU OKAY?
OKAY? Ha, YEAH, I'M PRETTY OKAY.
I MEAN, SO ME AND HIPP ENDED UP HANGING OUT AFTER WE LEFT THE COFFEE SHOP YESTERDAY.
TALKED ABOUT HIS BAND, HOW IT GOT CRAZY. THE ALBUM, RADIO PLAY, THE TOURS...
Y'KNOW, THE EGOS INVOLVED.
SO, WE ENDED UP GETTING DINNER, AND DRINKS, AND...
...
ANYWAY.
I THINK I LIKE HIM.
JON?
Uh, THAT'S... THAT'S REALLY GOOD, TABBY.
I'M REALLY GLAD YOU'RE OKAY.
OKAY, WHAT'S THAT ABOUT? WHY ARE YOU SO CONCERNED THAT I'M ALL RIGHT?
IS IT THAT WOLF THING?
I THINK THAT MIGHT BE OVERBLOWN.
TABBY, IT'S NOT OVERBLOWN. IT'S--I--
I GOTTA TALK TO YOU. CAN WE MEET SOMEWHERE?
GOD, JON, LOOK, I... WAS SUPER LATE TO WORK TODAY. I'VE GOT A MOUNTAIN OF THINGS TO DO.
CAN WE CATCH UP TOMORROW OR SOMETHING?
JON?
TOMORROW GOOD FOR YOU?
Uh...
Oh, HOLD ON A SEC, JON.
(WHAT'S UP?)
(YEAH. SORRY, SIR--I'M JUST GETTING OFF NOW.)
JON, I GOTTA GO. I'LL TALK TO YOU SOON, OKAY?
KLIK

KTUNK
WHERE--
WHERE IS GONNA HOLD ME...?
QUI VIVE
JONATHAN'S ROOM STAY OUT COOL DUDES ONLY
DO NOT ENTER
KLIK
WEEOOP
Oh GOD.
I'M HERE.
I'M UNARMED. I-I'M PEACEFUL.
JESUS, TURBO.
NOT EVERY-THING'S ABOUT YOU.

LOOK AROUND FOR ONCE, WILL YA?
EMERGENCY CALL 911 FIRE
POLICE
WH-- THAT WASN'T THERE BEFORE--
NO SHIT, JON-BOY.
THIS DINGUS JUST DID IT. HE'S FAST AS HELL WITH HIS LITTLE BLACK SPRAY PAINT.
IT'S RED PAINT! RED! DON'T YOU ASSHOLES FUCKING SEE
AAAKK

SHUT IT. YOU WANNA CATCH ANOTHER CHARGE?
QUI-VIVE
GET IN THERE. SLEEP IT OFF.
NFF
POLICE
AND THE TOWN WILL BE SAFE FROM YOUR BULLSHIT, AT LEAST FOR ONE NIGHT.
SLAM
TELL ME ABOUT IT, MAN. I'M 'BOUT TO RUN IN ANYONE WHO LOOKS AT ME FUNNY.
JESUS. THIS TOWN. WHAT A FUCKING MESS.
I DON'T HAVE TO TELL YOU, TURBO. YOUR HOUSE WAS ALREADY PRETTY WELL FUCKED BEFORE FRANCISCO GOYA OVER THERE PUT HIS NUTS ON IT.
LISTEN, DYLAN, Y-YOU GUYS GOTTA ARREST ME. YOU GOTTA PUT ME IN A CELL.
O-OR SOMEWHE I'M SERIOU I-I-I'M--
HA. SURE THING, TURBO. Oh--
...YOU HEAR WHAT THAT THING DID TO PASTOR STEPHEN?
Oh GOD.
I-IS HE OKAY?
PFF!
I'M NOT SUPPOSED TO SAY. BUT YEAH, UNFORTUNATELY.
I'M JUST SAYIN'-- THAT THING GOES ON TO TAKE DOWN MS. MILLER? ALL MY HIGH SCHOOL GRUDGES ARE SETTLED.
THAT'S ONE FUCKED-UP GUARDIAN ANGEL YOU GOT.
YOU AIN'T LYIN'.
ALL RIGHT, LET'S MOTOR. LATER, TURB--

KRAK
QUI-VIVE
POLICE
GOD DAMN IT--
HOUFF
THUMP
KRICK
SHOVE
TOSS

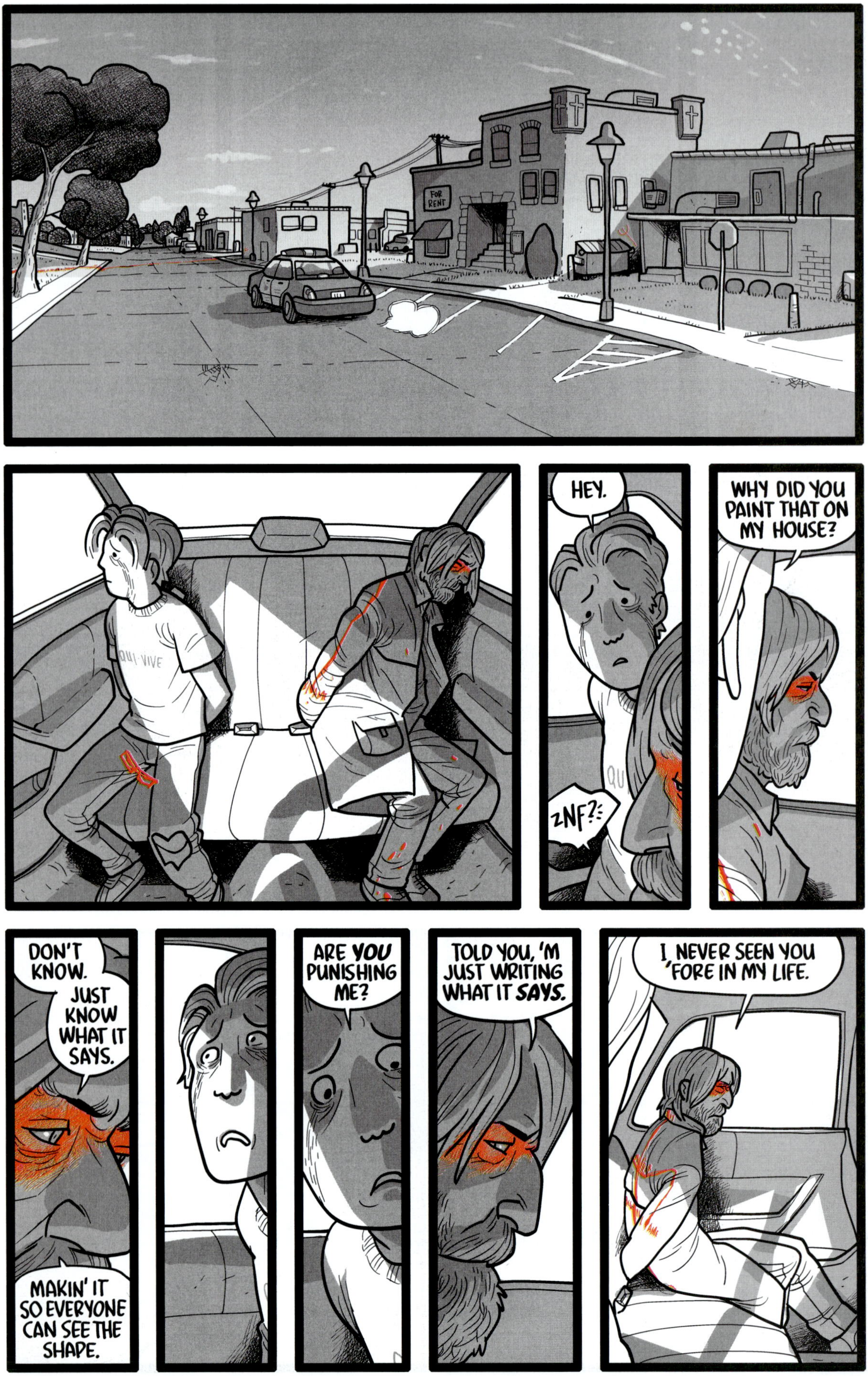
FOR RENT
QUI-VIVE
HEY.
ZNF?
WHY DID YOU PAINT THAT ON MY HOUSE?
DON'T KNOW.
JUST KNOW WHAT IT SAYS.
MAKIN' IT SO EVERYONE CAN SEE THE SHAPE.
ARE YOU PUNISHING ME?
TOLD YOU, 'M JUST WRITING WHAT IT SAYS.
I NEVER SEEN YOU 'FORE IN MY LIFE.

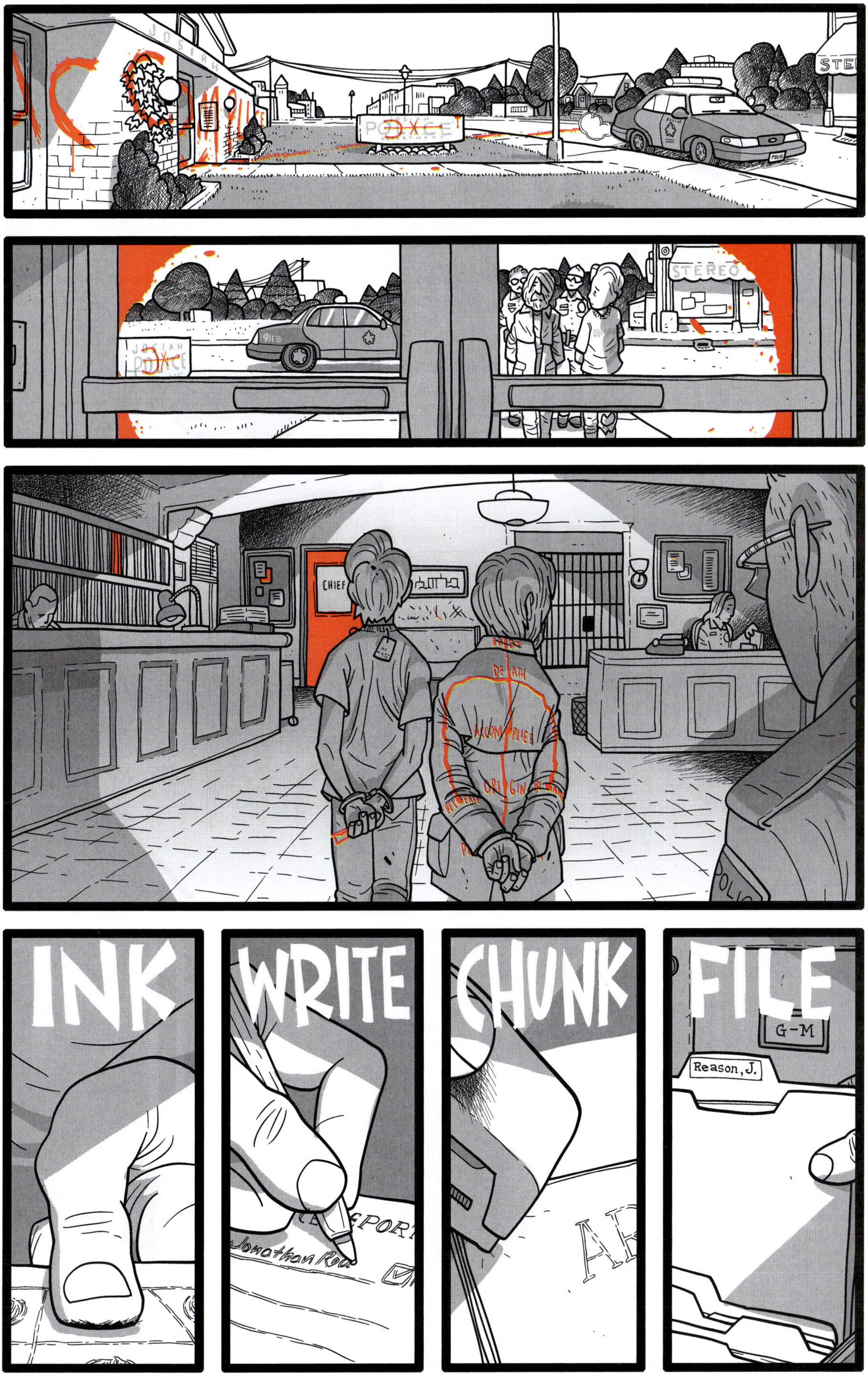

JOSIAH
POLICE
STEREO
CHIEF
INK
WRITE
CHUNK
FILE
G-M
Reason, J.

ALL RIGHT. BOTH OF YOU.
CELL THREE.
WAIT, NO.
NO, NO, I NEED MY OWN SPACE. I CAN'T BE IN THERE WITH HIM.
THAT'S NOT--
I CAN'T BE IN THERE WITH HIM!!
MOTHERFU Y'THINK BETTER TH ME?
FOR GOD'S SAKE, JONATHAN. GET IN THERE.
NO!
NO
GOD DAMN IT--
NO--
SLAM
JESUS. FINE.
HE GOES IN TWO.
TURBO HERE GOES IN THREE.

THANK GOD.
...THANK...
END CHAPTER TWO

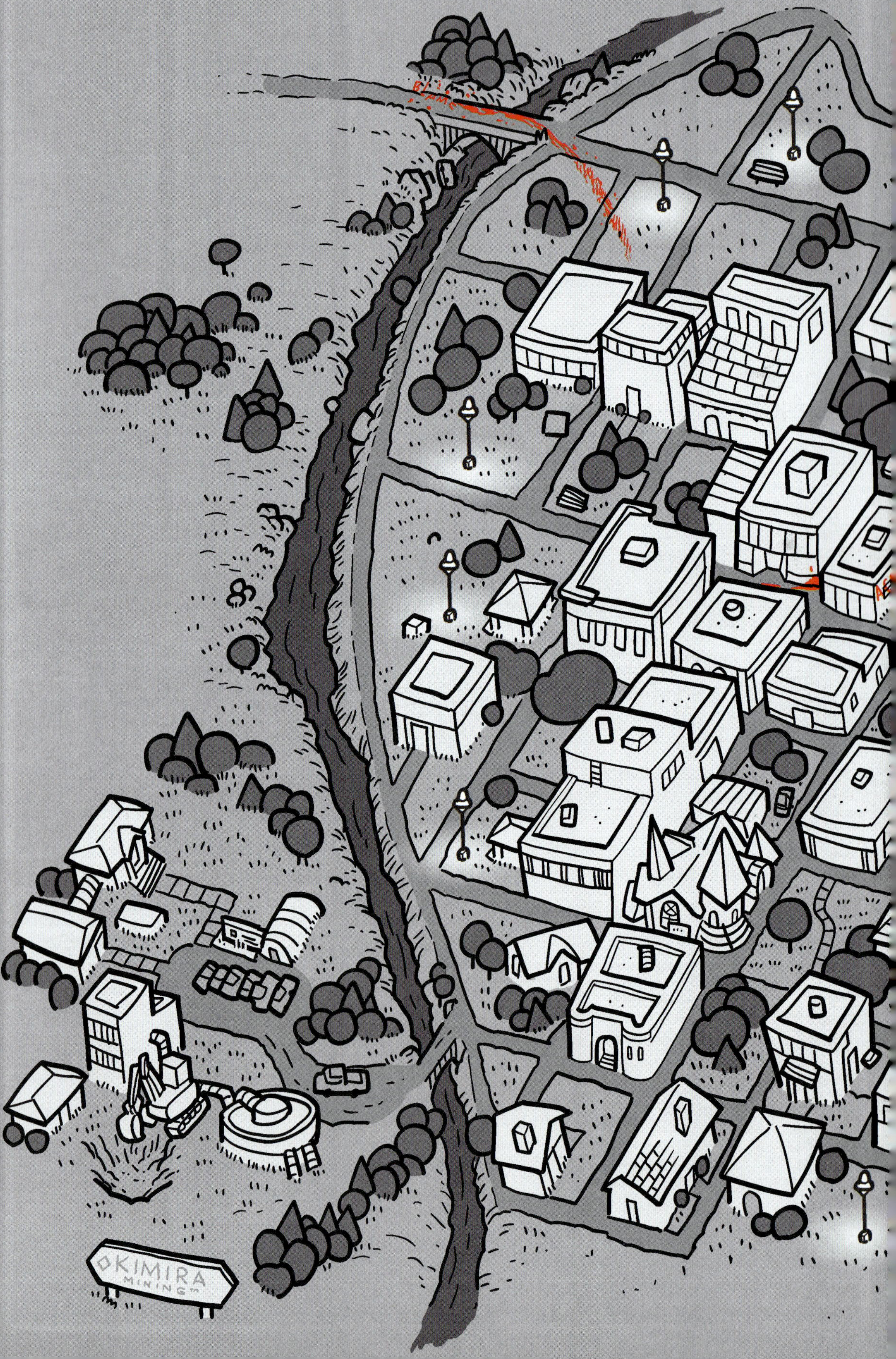
KIMIRA
MINING™

THREE

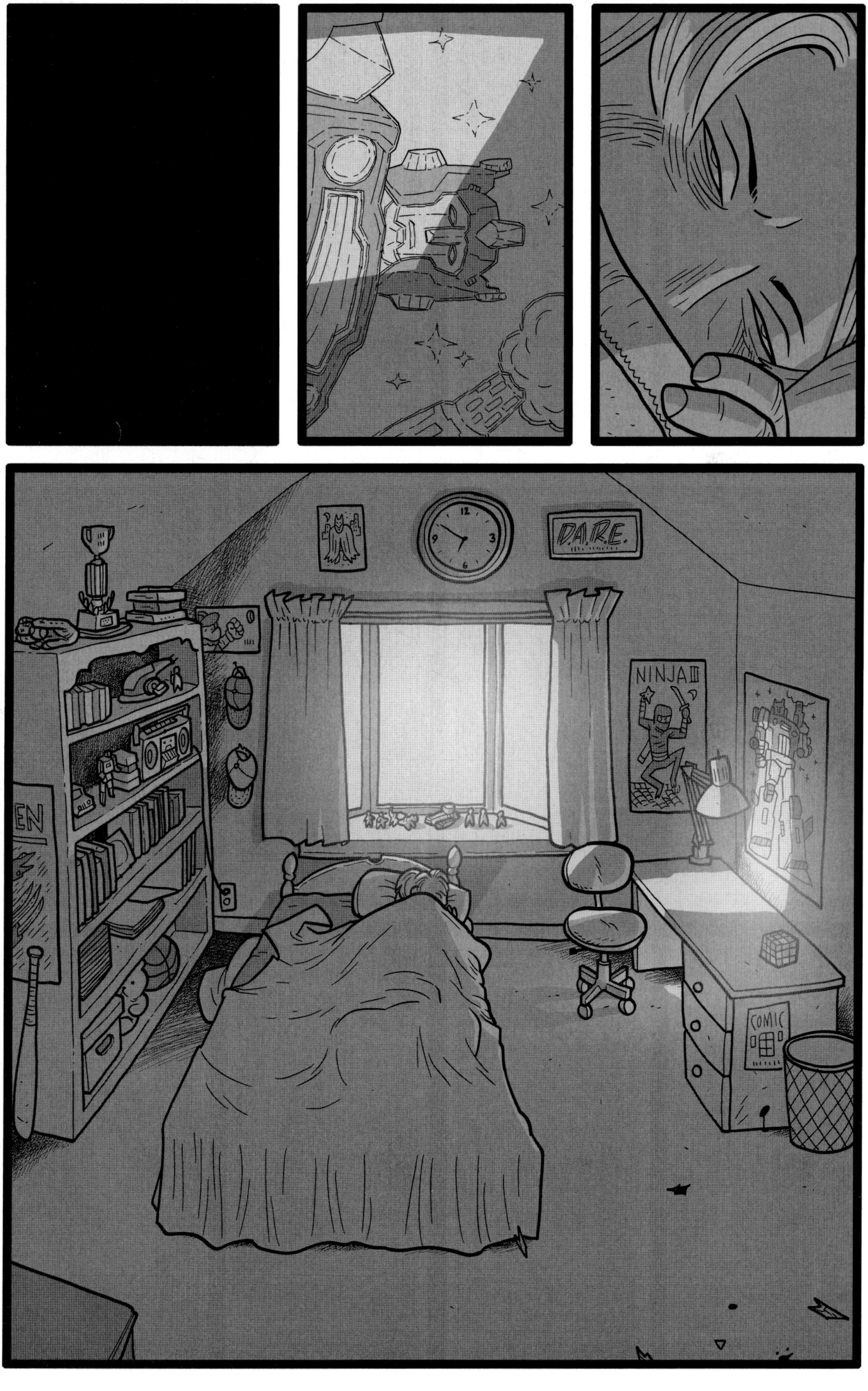
D.A.R.E.
NINJA III
COMIC

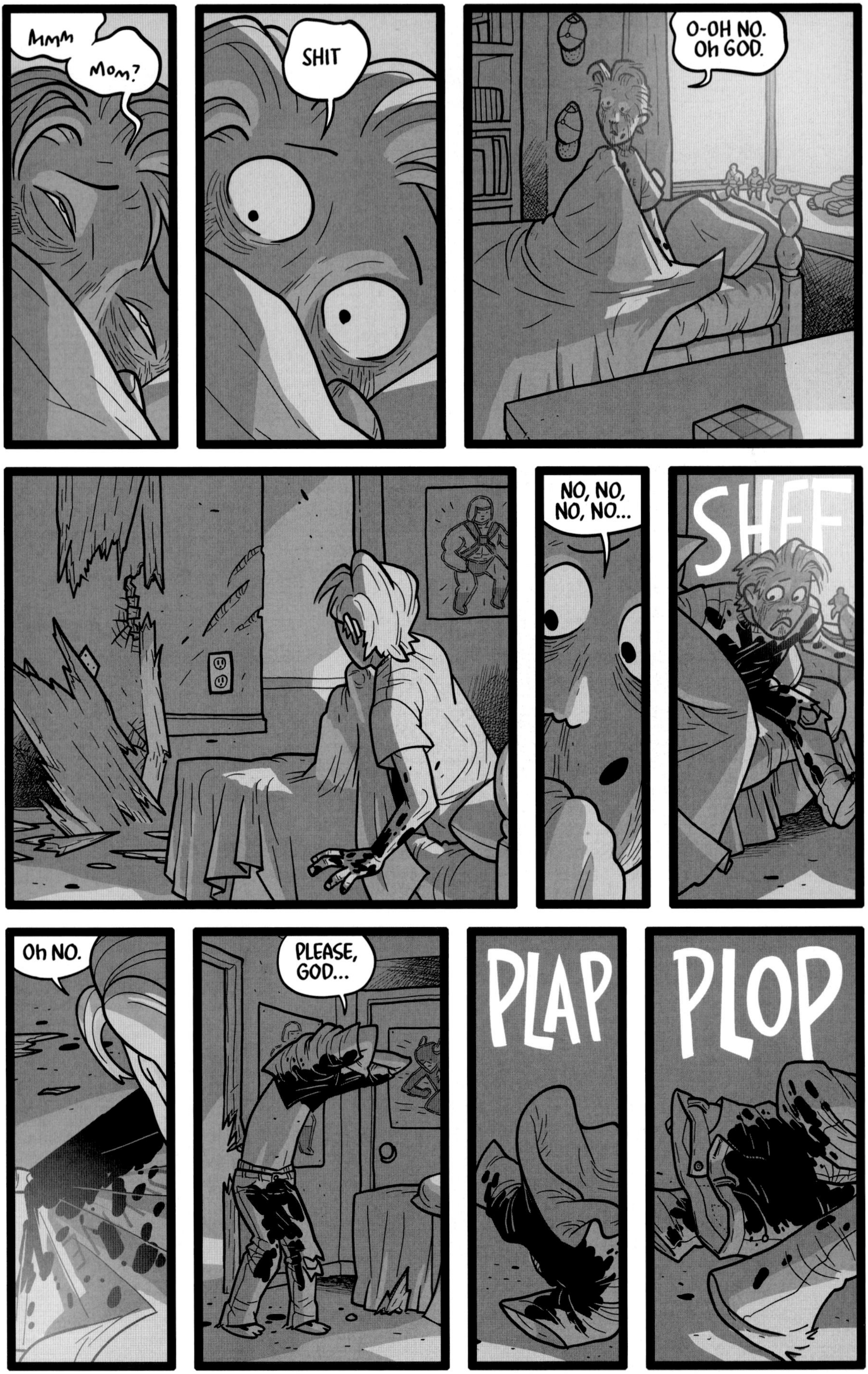

Mmm
Mom?
SHIT
O-OH NO. Oh GOD.
NO, NO, NO, NO...
SHFF
Oh NO.
PLEASE, GOD...
PLAP
PLOP

Oh GOD, oh GOD
OG BLANKETING THE
AL STATE AREAS ALONG
NGOR RIVER, WITH LOW
BILITY ON THE ROADS.
LET'S BE **CAREFUL** OUT THERE, huh, VIEWERS?

TUESDAY

VER HIGH SCHOOL
ORIGIN

JOSIAH
Oh GOD Oh GOD Oh GOD
Oh GOD, D-DYLAN?
Oh MY G--
H-HELLO?
I-IS SOMEONE OUT THERE?

I-I'M LOCKED IN HERE--ARE THERE KEYS?
HELLO?
CHING
P-PLEASE, I DON'T KNOW WHAT'S GOING ON OUT THERE, B-BUT...
S-SOMETHING HAPPENED. S-SOMETHING TERRIBLE.
PLEASE, I-I-I GOTTA GET OUT OF HERE.
PLEASE. WHOEVER YOU ARE, LEMME OU--
Oh, NO.
WAIT--
NO.
NO, NO.
GET AWAY FROM ME.
2
3
WAIT, WAIT--
NO! GET AWAY FROM ME!
PLEASE! WHAT HAPPENED?
NO NO NO
I-I-I'M LEAVING THE KEYS HERE.
I-I'M SORRY.
I'M SORRY.
I'M SORRY.
I'M SORRY.

I'M SORRY.
JOSIAH
CHIEF
I'M SO SORRY.

KTAK
EPIALOS LABS
biomedical solutions
800 OLD HWY 6
HEY, C'MON--
Uh...
GEEZ, YOU LOOK TERRIBLE.
DID YOU SLEEP OKAY?
...
...NO.
NOT REALLY.

IT'S JUST THROUGH HERE.
HERE, HAVE A SEAT.
LET ME GRAB YOU SOME WATER.

TABBY, I...
I DID SOMETHING TERRIBLE.
YOU?
TSSH
C'MON.
I DID.
TH-THE COPS CAME TO MY HOUSE.
I-IT WAS DYLAN. I-I'VE KNOWN HIM SINCE WE WERE FIVE YEARS OLD.
HE ARRESTED ME.
I-I MEAN, I WANTED HIM TO.
I-I PUNCHED HIM, AND HE PUT ME IN A CELL.
AND I THOUGHT IT WAS ALL GOING TO BE SAFE, B-BUT--
M-MY GOD...
OKAY. SO HE PUT YOU IN A CELL. AND YOU'RE HERE NOW.
HOW'D YOU GET OUT?
I-- TABBY...
YOU'RE NEVER GOING TO LOOK AT ME THE SAME.
OKAY.
FIRST OF ALL, IF YOU PUNCHED DYLAN BRYSON IN THE FACE, YOU DID AN AWESOME THING.
I HATE THAT GUY.

SECOND, I SEEM TO RECALL THAT YOU'RE THE PERSON WHO FISHED THOSE TWO BABY RACCOONS OUT OF HIS STORM DRAIN, IN THE MIDDLE OF THE NIGHT.
I DEFINITELY REMEMBER DRIVING YOU TO THE E.R. FOR A RABIES SHOT.
SO. I KNOW WHAT KIND OF PERSON YOU ARE.
A GOOD ONE.
WHO DOES ANNOYING THINGS FOR GOOD REASONS.
OKAY, BUT I--
BABE!
K-CHUNK
HIPP!
HEYY...
WHAT ARE YOU DOING HERE?
HOW'D YOU GET IN?
Uh, WHAT'S-HER-FACE WAS GOING OUT, BUT--
BUT BABE. HAVEN'T YOU HEARD?
NO, WHAT?
JESUS, TAB, IT'S A FUCKING MESS OUT THERE.
IT'S THAT THING.
WHAT, THE WOLF THING?
IT AIN'T A FUCKING WOLF.
BELIEVE ME.
BLOOD'S BEEN SPILLED, TAB. WE'RE PUTTING TOGETHER A POSSE TO--
:snicker: A POSSE? WHAT ARE YOU, COWBOYS?
BABE.
YOU DON'T GET IT.
THE POLICE STATION'S GONE.
IT'S FUCKING DESTROYED.
MY DAD'S THERE NOW. HE WOULDN'T TELL ME ANYTHING ELSE BEFORE HE LEFT.

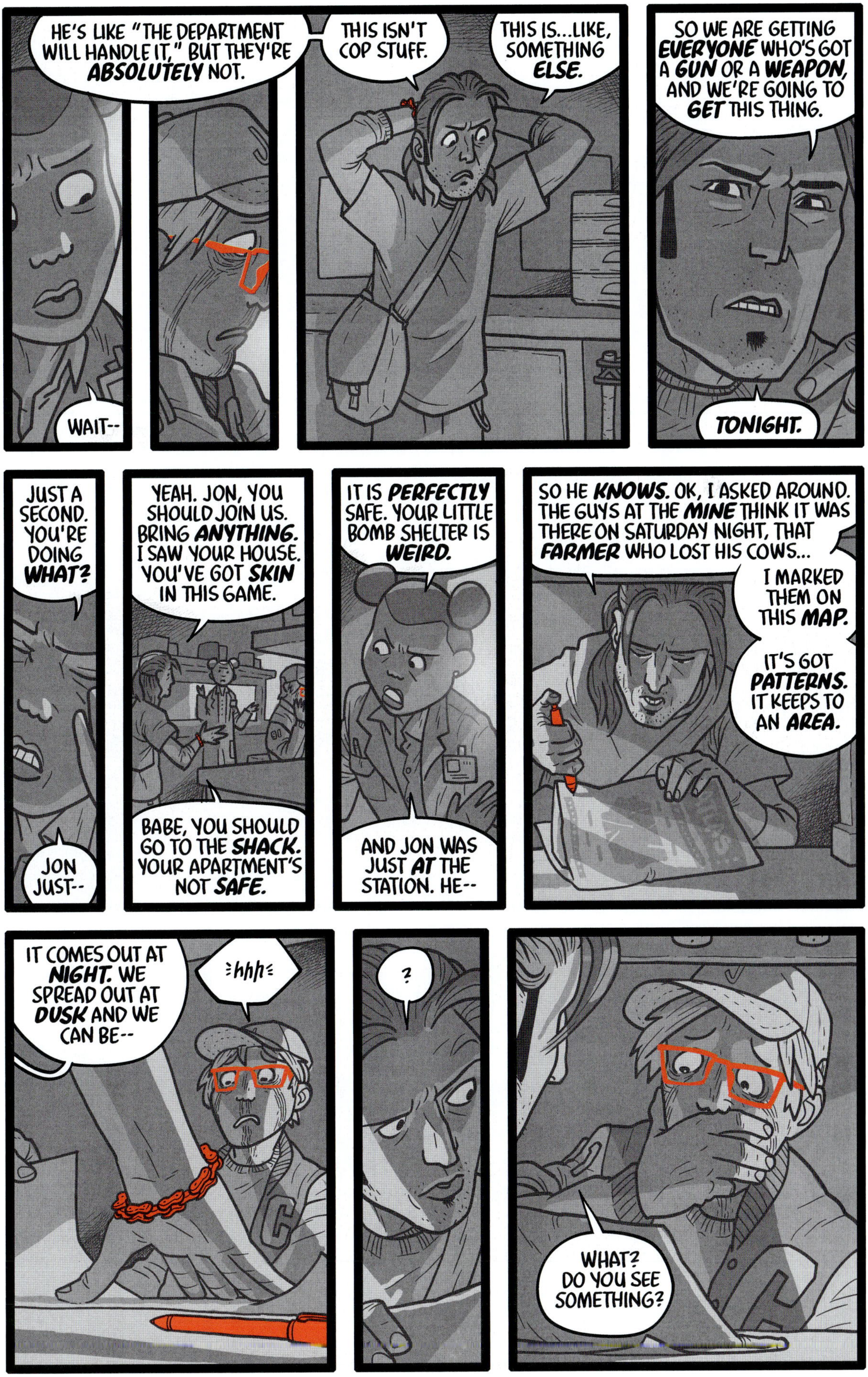
HE'S LIKE "THE DEPARTMENT WILL HANDLE IT," BUT THEY'RE ABSOLUTELY NOT.
WAIT--
THIS ISN'T COP STUFF.
THIS IS...LIKE, SOMETHING ELSE.
SO WE ARE GETTING EVERYONE WHO'S GOT A GUN OR A WEAPON, AND WE'RE GOING TO GET THIS THING.
TONIGHT.
JUST A SECOND. YOU'RE DOING WHAT?
JON JUST--
YEAH. JON, YOU SHOULD JOIN US. BRING ANYTHING. I SAW YOUR HOUSE. YOU'VE GOT SKIN IN THIS GAME.
BABE, YOU SHOULD GO TO THE SHACK. YOUR APARTMENT'S NOT SAFE.
IT IS PERFECTLY SAFE. YOUR LITTLE BOMB SHELTER IS WEIRD.
AND JON WAS JUST AT THE STATION. HE--
SO HE KNOWS. OK, I ASKED AROUND. THE GUYS AT THE MINE THINK IT WAS THERE ON SATURDAY NIGHT, THAT FARMER WHO LOST HIS COWS...
I MARKED THEM ON THIS MAP.
IT'S GOT PATTERNS. IT KEEPS TO AN AREA.
IT COMES OUT AT NIGHT. WE SPREAD OUT AT DUSK AND WE CAN BE--
hhh
?
WHAT? DO YOU SEE SOMETHING?

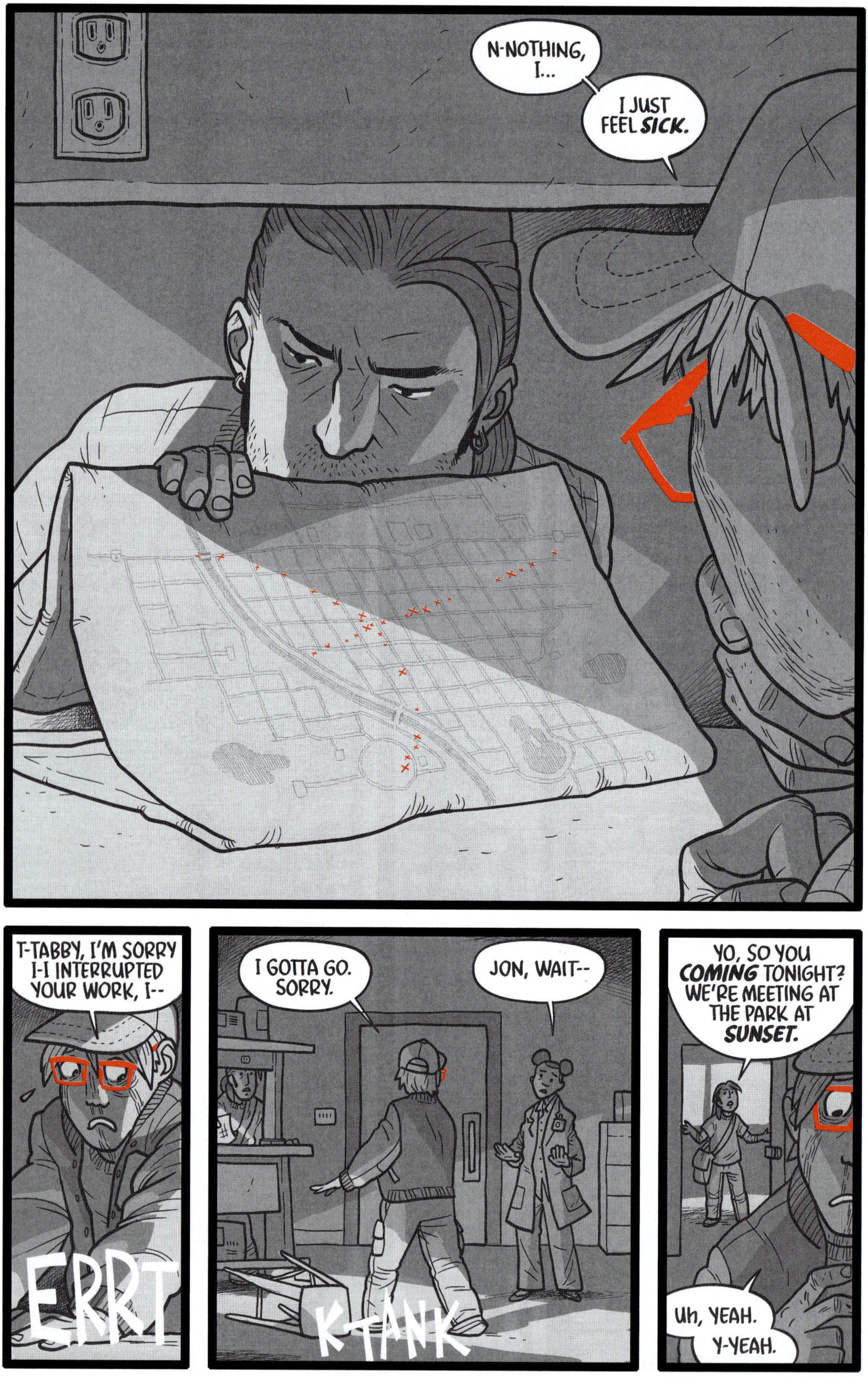
N-NOTHING, I...
I JUST FEEL SICK.
T-TABBY, I'M SORRY I-I INTERRUPTED YOUR WORK, I--
ERRT
I GOTTA GO. SORRY.
JON, WAIT--
K-TANK
YO, SO YOU COMING TONIGHT? WE'RE MEETING AT THE PARK AT SUNSET.
Uh, YEAH.
Y-YEAH.

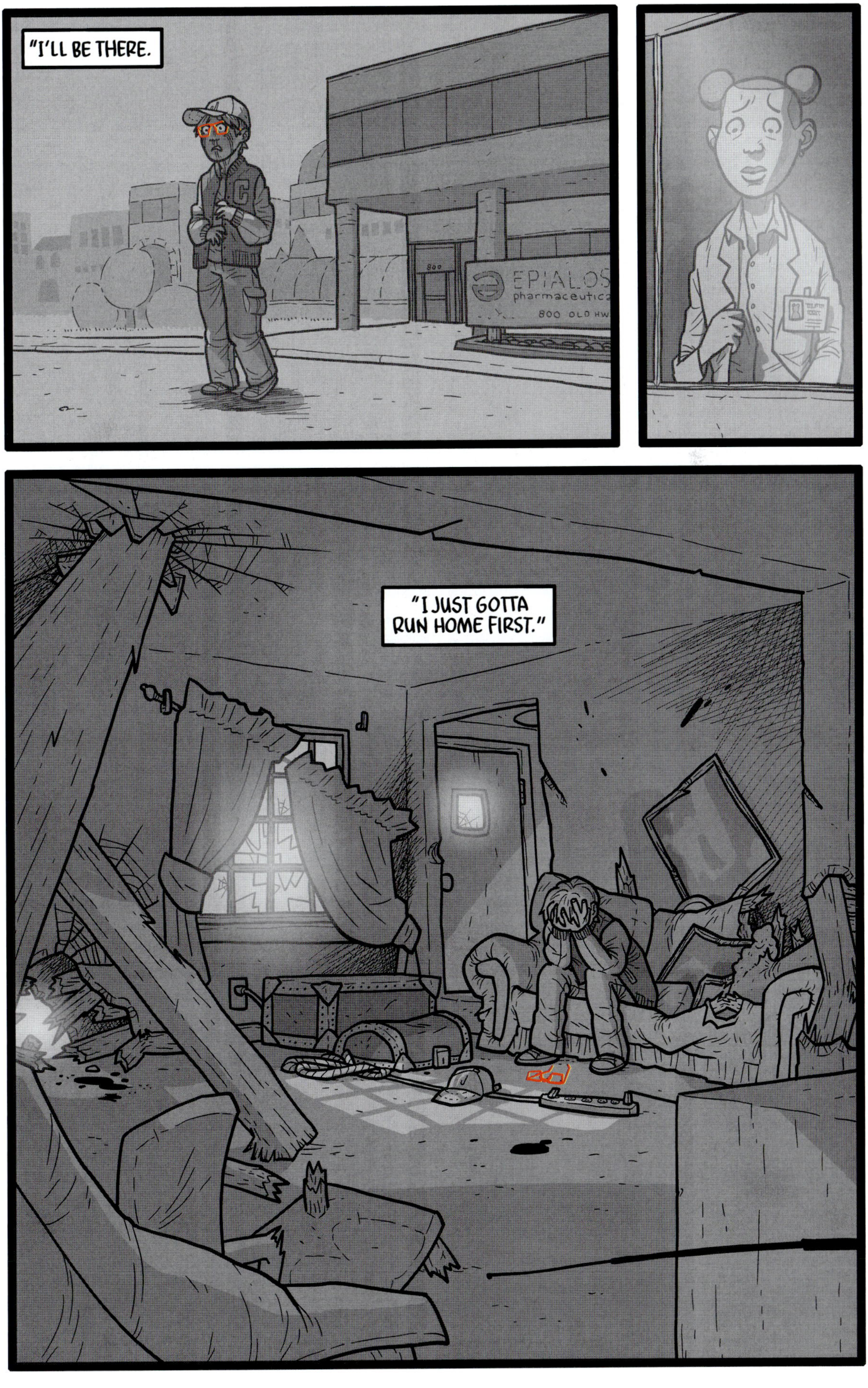
"I'LL BE THERE.
800
EPIALOS
pharmaceutica
800 OLD HW
"I JUST GOTTA RUN HOME FIRST."

STUFF
K-KLUNK
SORRY

GH SCHOOL
--THIS GOOD ENOUGH?
--FOR **DYLAN**--
--A .30-06. DON'T WORRY, IT'LL STOP **ANYTHING**--
--SHOW THIS SON OF A BITCH IT CHOSE THE WRONG GOD DAMN **TOWN**--
--SAY IT'S GOTTA BE TWELVE FEET **TALL**--
--**BEAR**, MAYBE--

THING--
FOR ALL--
--BY THE RIVER--
REALTY
THIRD EYE
OPTICAL
WHAT
GONNA GET CAUGHT
SOME OF
SHIT

SHH! SHH
WHAT?
DO IT, Y' FUCKIN' PIECE OF SHIT.

I AM.
BLAME
RIP
KILLER
BLAME

sniff
TIE
sniff
WHOO

I'M SORRY, LORD.
I'M SO SORRY.
I'VE ALWAYS TRIED TO LIVE IN YOUR LIGHT.
BY YOUR EXAMPLE.
HOW TO BE GOOD...
...HOW NOT TO **FALL**.
I **ALWAYS** TRIED.
I-I PROMISE.
HA. *sniff*
YOU KNOW IF I'M TELLING THE TRUTH.
EVERYTHING GOOD COMES FROM YOU. **ALWAYS.**
MOM KNEW THAT, OF COURSE.
DAD... SOMETIMES.
I LOVE YOU.
I THANK YOU FOR THIS LIFE.
I WISH IT COULD HAVE BEEN LONGER.
AMEN.

END of CHAPTER THREE

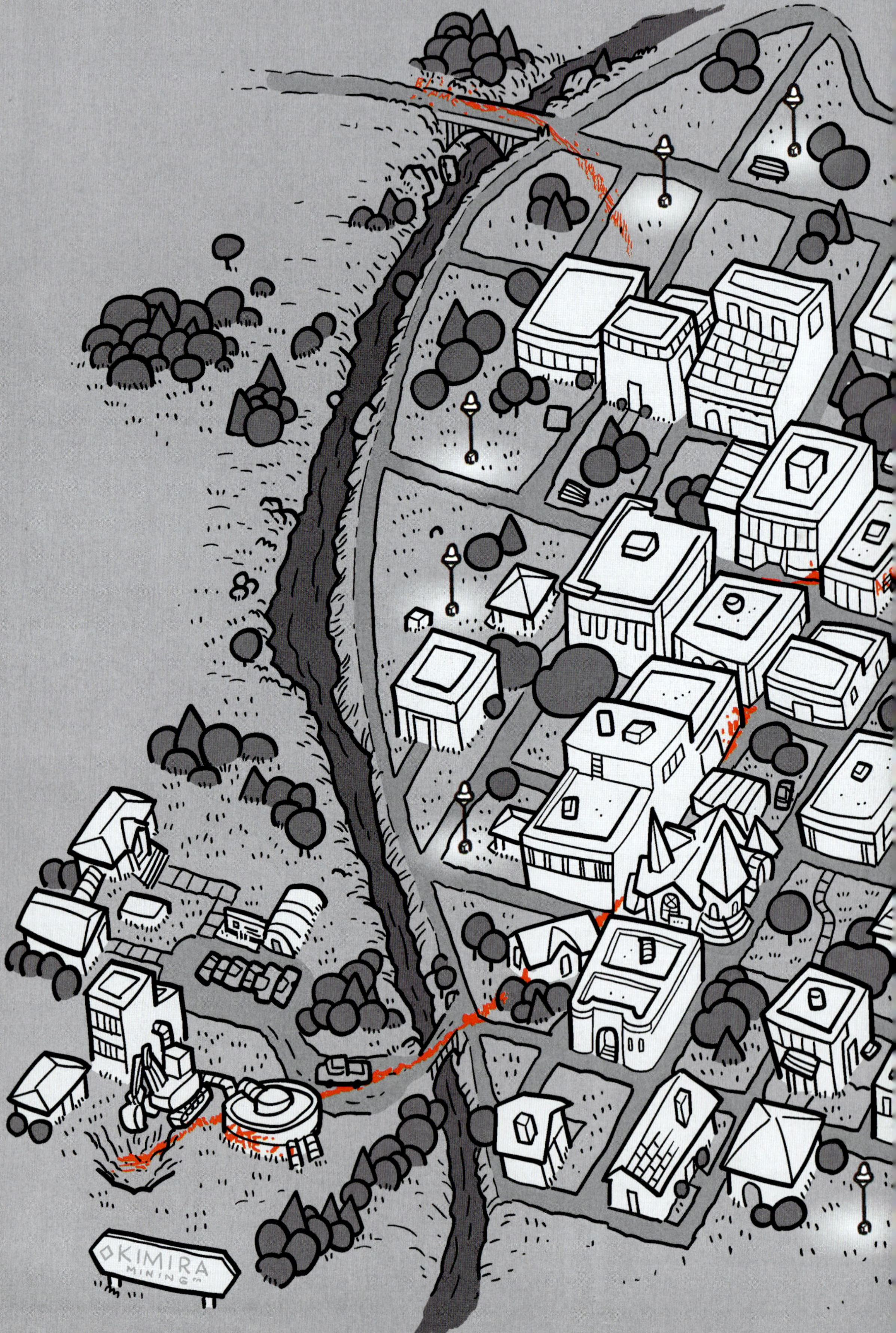
KIMIRA
MINING

FOUR

ERRNT
ERRNT
ERRNT
ERRNT
KLIK
VRRN
NNNNNNNN
NNNNN
NNNNNN
NNNNN

WEDNESDAY

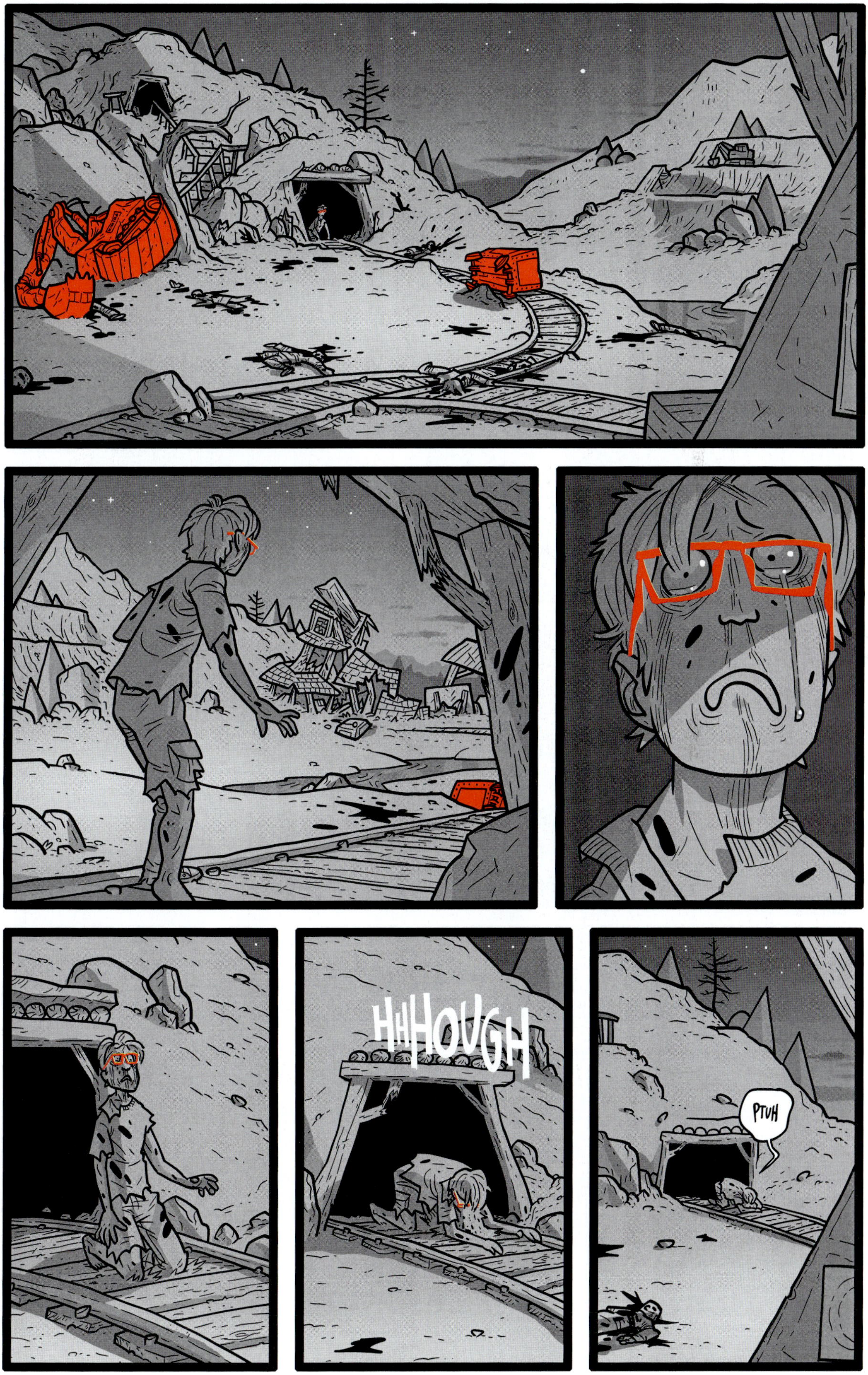
HHHOUGH
PTUH

HUUARCH
YOU HAVE A GUN.
GO.
F-FUCKING GO.

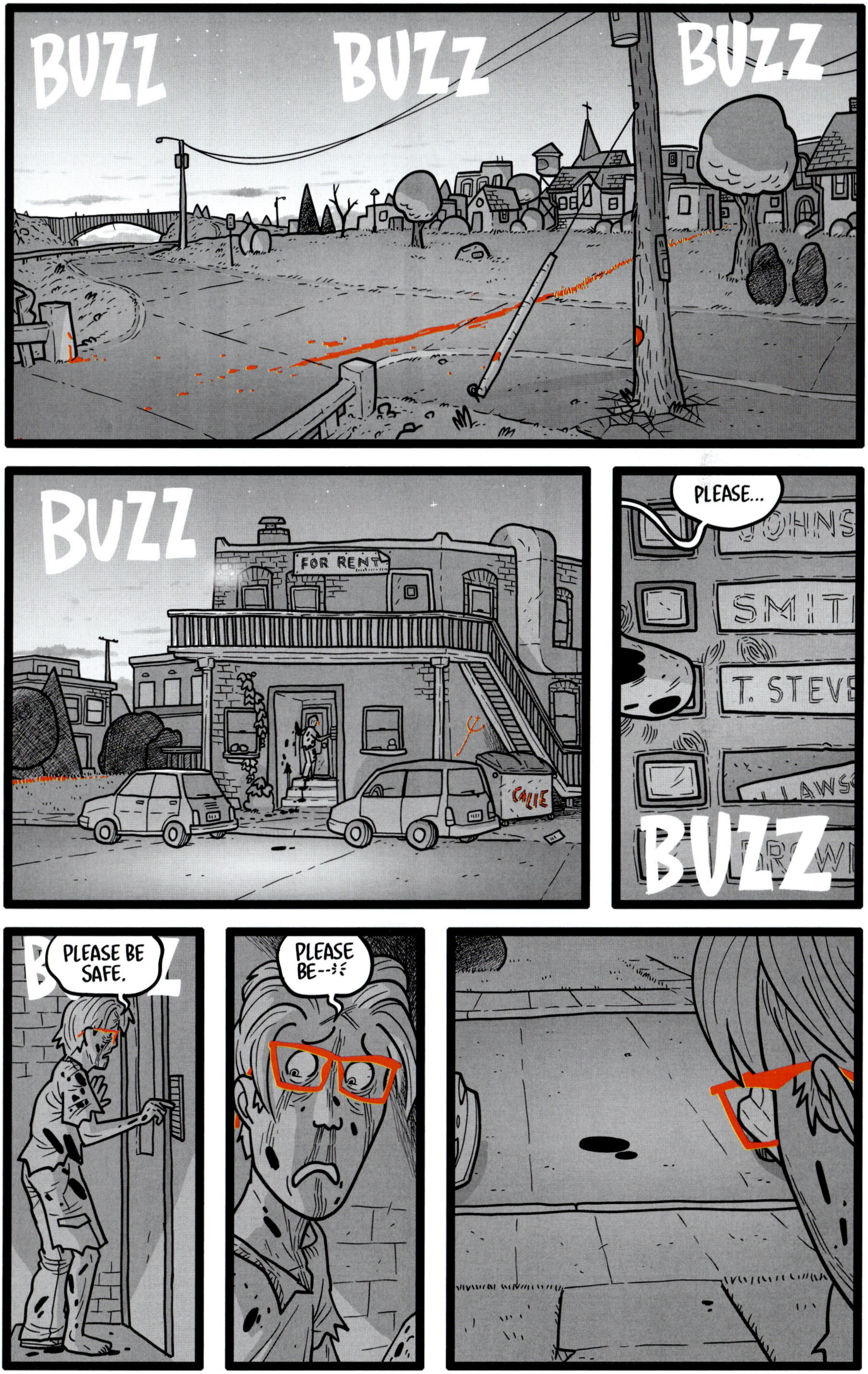
BUZZ
BUZZ
BUZZ
BUZZ
FOR RENT
CALIE
PLEASE...
JOHNS
SMIT
T. STEVE
LAWS
BUZZ
PLEASE BE SAFE.
PLEASE BE--

JOSIAH, IOWA
Home of the Tigers
NICOLI
Oh MY GOD.
YOU'RE ALIVE.
I HEARD IT.
ALL THE SCREAMING. I--
I COULD HEAR EVERYTHING.
C-COME IN. WE CAN'T BE OUT HERE. WE HAVE TO WAIT FOR--
Oh GOD, WHERE'S HIPP?
IS HE OKAY?
I... I DON'T KNOW.
I DON'T KNOW ANYTHING.

OKAY.
OKAY.
HERE'S A CLOTH IF YOU WANT TO GET CLEANED UP.
TSSH
FILES
MISSING
HERE.
NNF. LOOKS LIKE SOME OF THIS ISN'T COMING OFF. LET ME--
Oh, JESUS.
JESUS CHRIST, JON.
WHAT IS THIS? WHAT DID IT DO TO YOU?
WHAT KIND OF... THING COULD DO THIS TO YOU?

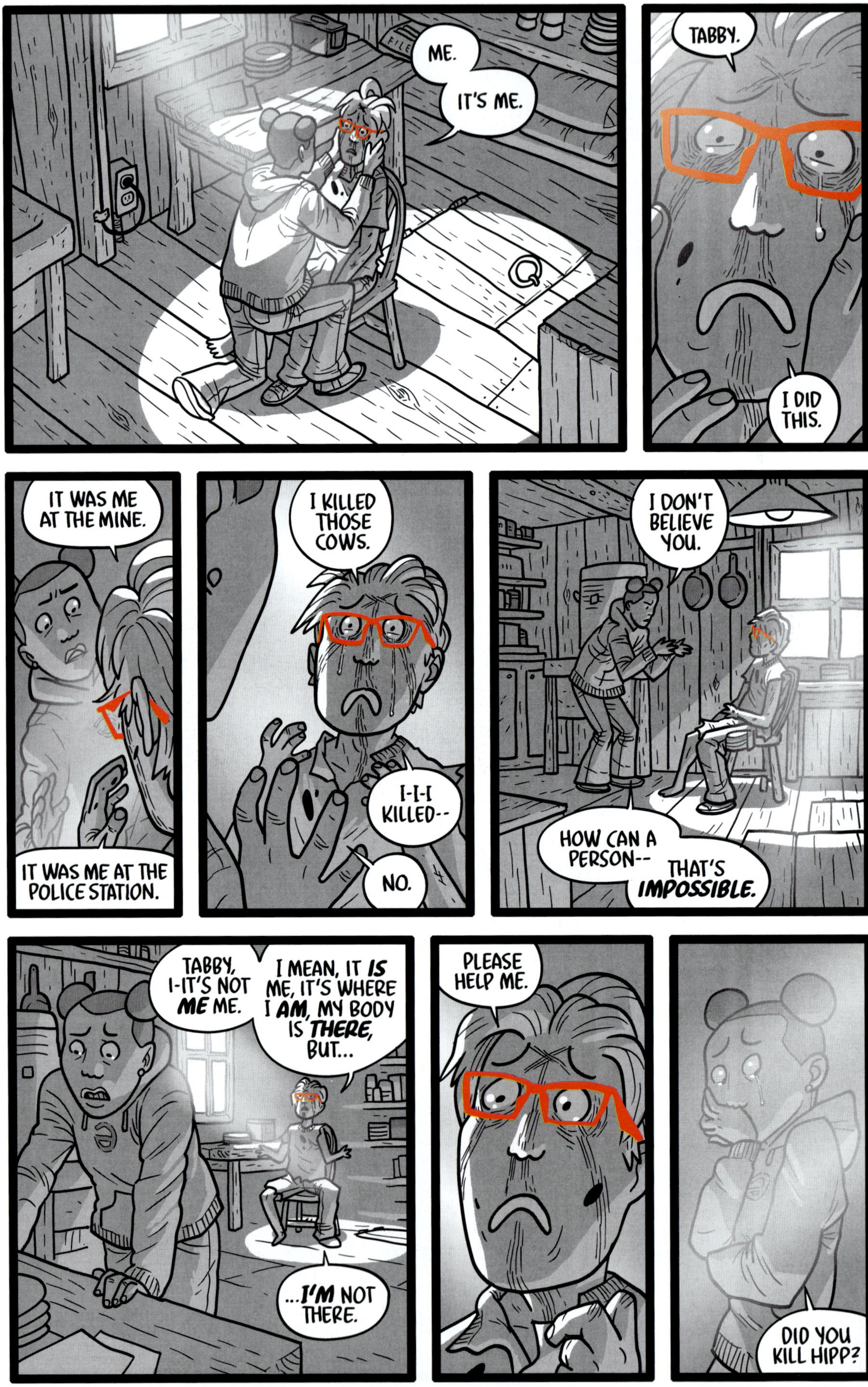
ME.
IT'S ME.
TABBY.
I DID THIS.
IT WAS ME AT THE MINE.
IT WAS ME AT THE POLICE STATION.
I KILLED THOSE COWS.
I-I-I KILLED--
NO.
I DON'T BELIEVE YOU.
HOW CAN A PERSON--
THAT'S IMPOSSIBLE.
TABBY, I-IT'S NOT ME ME.
I MEAN, IT IS ME, IT'S WHERE I AM, MY BODY IS THERE, BUT...
...I'M NOT THERE.
PLEASE HELP ME.
DID YOU KILL HIPP?

I DON'T THINK SO.
I-I DIDN'T-- I DIDN'T SEE HIM.
sniff
...
THAT'LL HAVE TO DO FOR NOW.
OKAY.
SO YOU'RE LOSING TIME.
THAT DOESN'T NECESSARILY MEAN ANY-THING.
ARE YOU DRINKING?
NO.
NO, OF COURSE NOT. OF COURSE NOT.
STUPID QUESTION.
O-OKAY, WELL, uh, SOMETIMES IT CAN BE A SIDE EFFECT OF SOME MEDICATIONS...
OR I-I MEAN, THERE ARE uh, SLEEP BEHAVIOR DISORDERS, LIKE, LIKE NIGHT TERRORS, LIKE--
TABBY.
I HANGED MYSELF, AND I WOKE UP ON A-A PILE OF MUTILATED BODIES.
IT'S NOT... SLEEPWALKING.
WELL, GOD DAMN IT, THERE HAS TO BE AN EXPLANATION!!
IF WE THINK ABOUT IT, I-IF WE THINK LOGICALLY ABOUT IT H-HARD ENOUGH, WE CAN FIGURE IT OUT!
SOMETHING'S CAUSING THIS TO HAPPEN. S-SO IF WE ELIMINATE THE IMPOSSIBLE STUFF, THEN WHAT WE'RE LEFT WITH, I-IT'S...
THAT'S THE TRUTH.
THAT'S SCIENCE. THAT'S WHERE THE ANSWER IS. IT'S GOTTA BE, IT'S--
BONG

BONG BONG BONG
WHY ARE THEY RINGING THE BELLS?
IT'S WEDNESDAY MORNING, IT'S--
SANCTUARY.
WHAT?
IT'S SANCTUARY.
THE CHURCH IS SAFE.

THAT'S WHERE WE HAVE TO GO.
THAT'S WHERE HIPP IS.
THAT'S WHERE THE ANSWER IS.
I DON'T THINK THAT'S A GOOD IDEA. WE HAVE TO FIGURE OUT WHAT'S GOING ON WITH YOU BEFORE WE CAN RISK--
TABBY, THIS THING THAT'S IN ME...
IT'S EVIL. IT'S DARKNESS.
EVERY SECOND IT'S IN THERE IT'S CHIPPING A PIECE OF ME AWAY.
THIS ISN'T SCIENCE. THERE ISN'T A MEDICINE OR-OR A TREATMENT FOR IT.
BUT THE CHURCH, BUT GOD, HE DRIVES EVIL OUT. I-IT'S WHAT HE DOES.
I-I COULDN'T DO IT WITH-- WITH VIOLENCE-- B-BUT THE CHURCH SAYS HE CAN DO IT WITH GOODNESS.
OKAY. OKAY.
BUT WHAT DO YOU THINK?
DO YOU THINK THIS WILL HELP YOU?
YEAH.
I DO.
THEN LET'S GO.
SLAM
LOCK
KCHK
VRM

YOU REALLY HANGED YOURSELF?
YEAH.
sniff
TABBY, I'M SORRY.
NOTHING ELSE WORKED.
KCHK
OKAY. WE'RE HERE.
I KNOW IF THERE'S ANSWERS HERE, YOU'RE GOING TO FIND 'EM.
BUT IF YOU CAN'T FIND WHAT YOU NEED, IF THIS ISN'T *IT*--
IT IS IT.
I-IT *IS.*
JON.
--THEN YOU *FIND* ME.
OKAY?
AND WE WILL GET THE HELL *OUT* OF HERE.
STOP
OKAY?
OKAY.
gasp
BABY!

OKAY, EVERYONE. LET'S MOVE IT INTO THE *CHURCH.*
PLENTY OF SPOTS IN THERE.
WE'VE GOT PLACES TO PUT BEDDING, AND WE CAN THEN GATHER IN THE uh, IN THE MAIN HALL.
NOW, THERE'S NO REASON TO THINK THERE'S ANY *DANGER* AT PRESENT.
BUT LET'S ah... KEEP IT *MOVING*, SHALL WE?
THERE ARE A LOT OF uh *UNKNOWNS* TO THIS SITUATION.

LOOKS LIKE YOU LEFT YOUR TRUNK OPEN, MARTY.
Huh. HOW ABOUT THAT.
WELL, YOU KNOW WHAT THEY SAY.
EASY COME, EASY GO.
I--DO YOU WANT ME TO SHUT IT?
SURE. DO AS YOU PLEASE.
TUNK
DON'T BE AFRAID, HONEY. THIS IS WHERE WE CAN BE SAFE.
WE HAVE TO BE BRAVE.
THE DEVIL WANTS US TO BE AFRAID.
NOTHING ANGERS HIM LIKE GOODNESS.
AND NOTHING MAKES HIM AS WEAK AS A FEARLESS HEART.

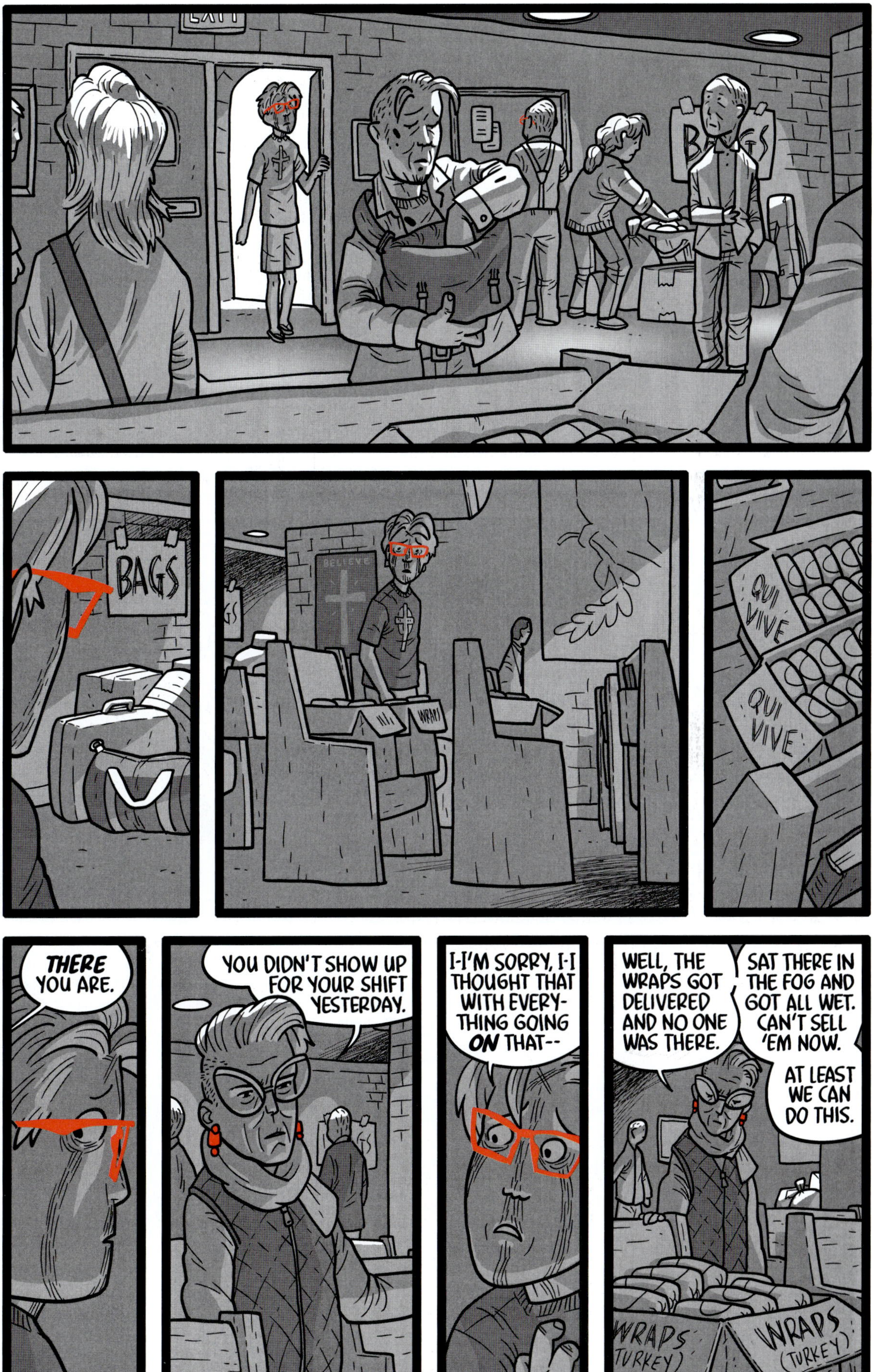
BAGS
BAGS
QUI VIVE
QUI VIVE
THERE YOU ARE.
YOU DIDN'T SHOW UP FOR YOUR SHIFT YESTERDAY.
I-I'M SORRY, I-I THOUGHT THAT WITH EVERY-THING GOING ON THAT--
WELL, THE WRAPS GOT DELIVERED AND NO ONE WAS THERE.
SAT THERE IN THE FOG AND GOT ALL WET. CAN'T SELL 'EM NOW.
AT LEAST WE CAN DO THIS.
WRAPS (TURKEY)
WRAPS (TURKEY)

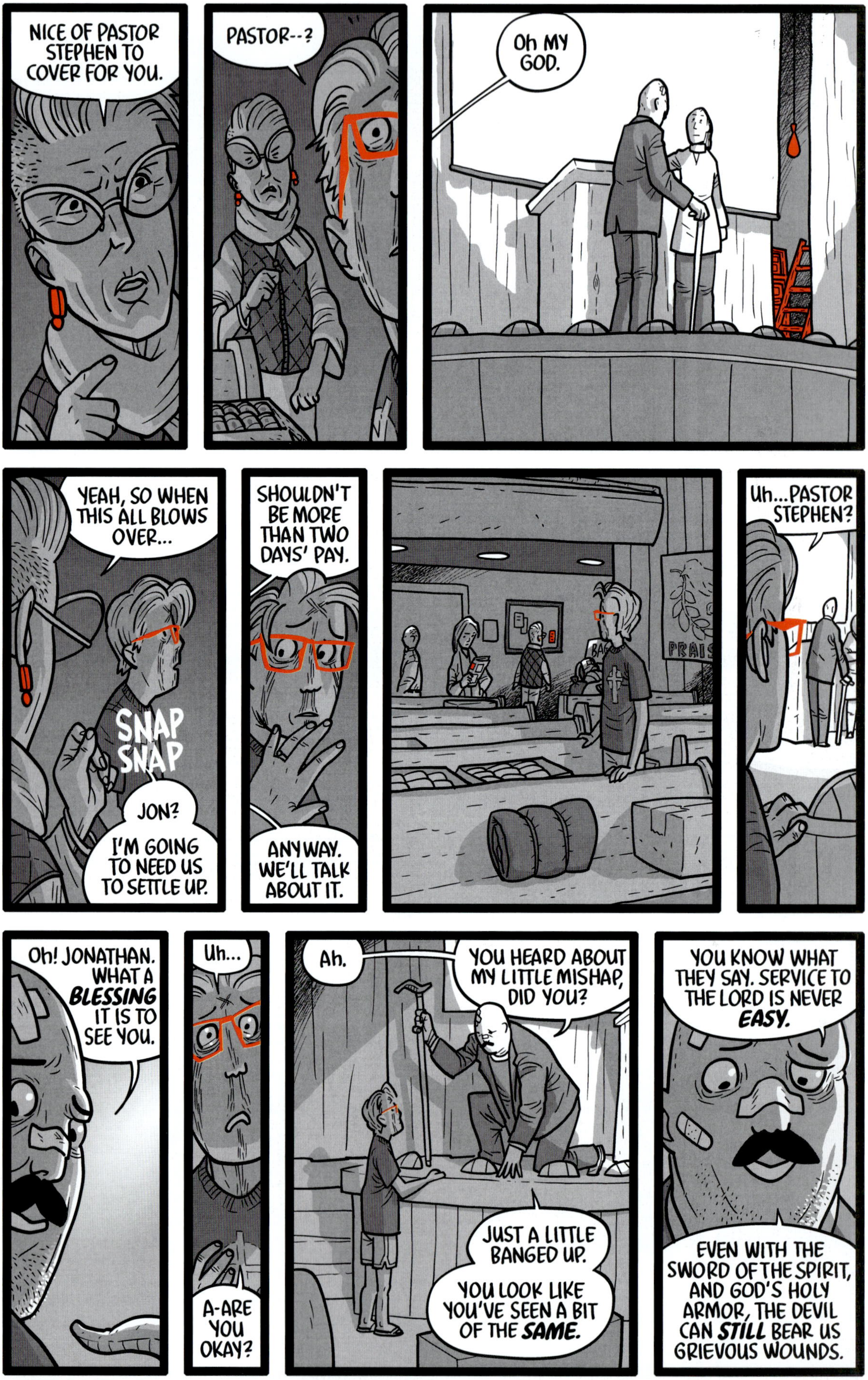
NICE OF PASTOR STEPHEN TO COVER FOR YOU.
PASTOR--?
Oh MY GOD.
YEAH, SO WHEN THIS ALL BLOWS OVER...
SNAP SNAP
JON?
I'M GOING TO NEED US TO SETTLE UP.
SHOULDN'T BE MORE THAN TWO DAYS' PAY.
ANYWAY. WE'LL TALK ABOUT IT.
PRAIS
Uh...PASTOR STEPHEN?
Oh! JONATHAN. WHAT A **BLESSING** IT IS TO SEE YOU.
Uh...
A-ARE YOU OKAY?
Ah.
YOU HEARD ABOUT MY LITTLE MISHAP, DID YOU?
JUST A LITTLE BANGED UP.
YOU LOOK LIKE YOU'VE SEEN A BIT OF THE **SAME.**
YOU KNOW WHAT THEY SAY. SERVICE TO THE LORD IS NEVER **EASY.**
EVEN WITH THE SWORD OF THE SPIRIT, AND GOD'S HOLY ARMOR, THE DEVIL CAN **STILL** BEAR US GRIEVOUS WOUNDS.

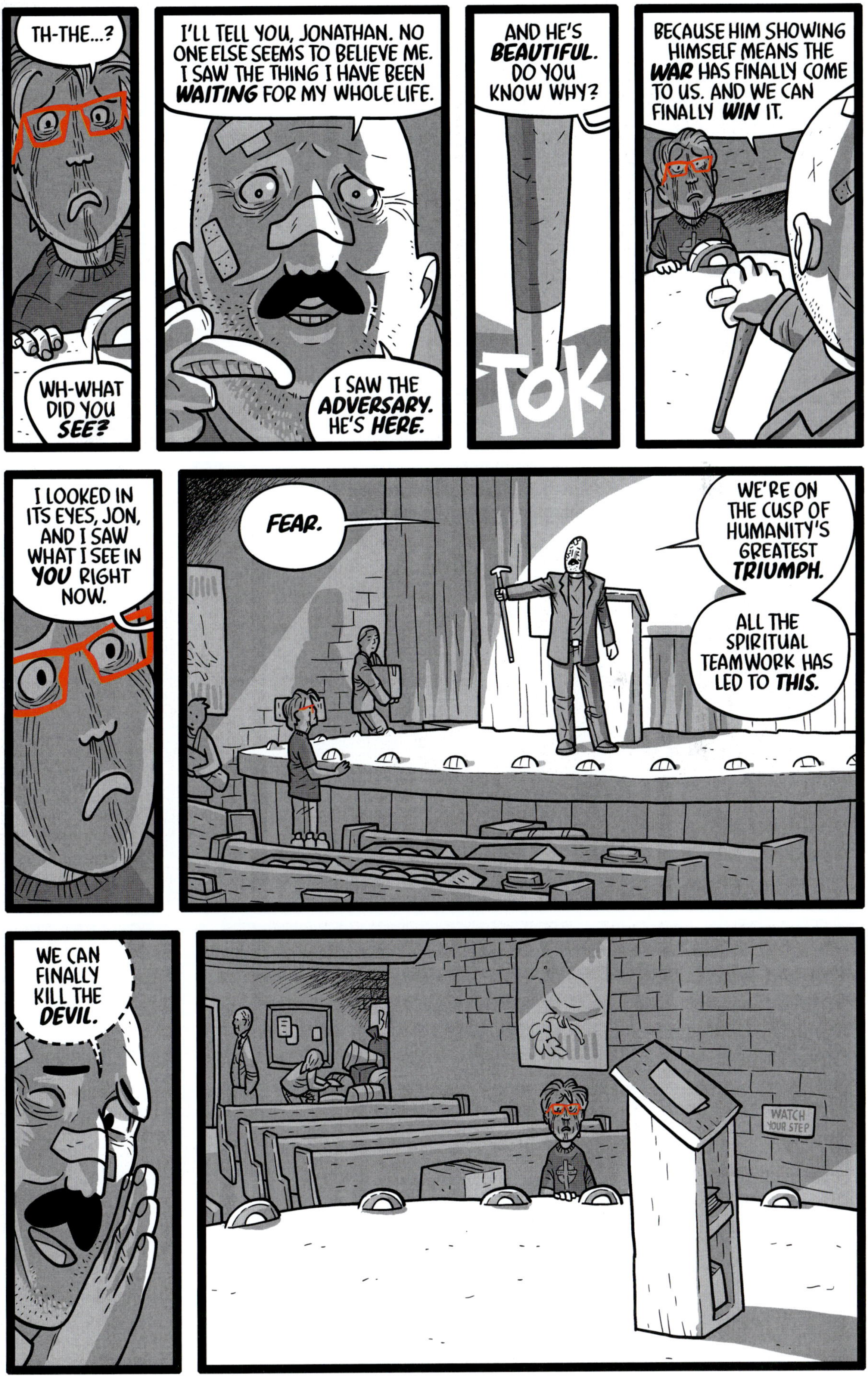
TH-THE...?
WH-WHAT DID YOU SEE?
I'LL TELL YOU, JONATHAN. NO ONE ELSE SEEMS TO BELIEVE ME. I SAW THE THING I HAVE BEEN WAITING FOR MY WHOLE LIFE.
I SAW THE ADVERSARY. HE'S HERE.
AND HE'S BEAUTIFUL. DO YOU KNOW WHY?
TOK
BECAUSE HIM SHOWING HIMSELF MEANS THE WAR HAS FINALLY COME TO US. AND WE CAN FINALLY WIN IT.
I LOOKED IN ITS EYES, JON, AND I SAW WHAT I SEE IN YOU RIGHT NOW.
FEAR.
WE'RE ON THE CUSP OF HUMANITY'S GREATEST TRIUMPH.
ALL THE SPIRITUAL TEAMWORK HAS LED TO THIS.
WE CAN FINALLY KILL THE DEVIL.
WATCH YOUR STEP

VOL 3
NOT RECOMMENDED
SIGILS AND YOU
DEMONOLOGY
PROTECTIVE SPELLS
SHFF
LESSER KEY
DEMONOLOGY
FLIPFLIP
SATANISM, huh?
THAP
I MIGHT HAVE KNOWN, FROM YOUR SINFUL LIFESTYLE.
Oh! Uh...
H-HI, KELLY.
EVERYTHING OKAY?
hup
YEAH, SURE, FINE. I HAVEN'T JOINED ANY ARMED MOBS LATELY, SO I'M STILL ALIVE.

SO DID MY MOM ALREADY BITCH YOU OUT ABOUT THE FUCKING WRAPS, OR IS SHE SAVING THAT FOR WHEN SHE'S GOT YOU TRAPPED HERE OVERNIGHT?
PLAP
TEEN Modest STYLE
FALL 1989
CALIE!
JOSIAH'S YOUNGEST VOLLEYBALL STAR
Uh, ha, YEAH, SHE BROUGHT IT UP.
I-I MEAN, I FEEL REALLY BAD ABOUT IT, BUT WE CAN SETTLE-
Oh JESUS, ARE YOU KIDDING? SHE'S ALREADY WRITTEN THAT SHIT OFF.
FIGURES SHE WOULDN'T LET YOU OFF THE HOOK.
FIFTY TENTH GRADERS A YEAR USED TO BEG HER TO TRY TO GET THEIR C+es ROUNDED UP. NO FUCKING DICE.
DIDN'T MATTER HOW MANY EARRINGS THEY MADE HER.
ANYWAY.
LEMME SEE THAT STUPID BOOK.
"O CHRISTIAN MANNE! PITY THOU YE POORE DIVIL! ALLE BUT BLINDE, AWASH IN SINNE, UNMOORED IN TYME, BUFFETTED BY HELLISH WINDS, SEEKING OUT GUYDANCE OF YE FELL SIGIL."
HUH! I TAKE IT BACK, JONATHAN. THIS RULES.
WHAT ELSE YA GOT OVER--
tump tump
EVERYONE ABLE TO HEAR ME?
WELCOME, EVERYONE. IF YOU'RE SURPRISED TO SEE ME OUT OF THE HOSPITAL, YOU'RE NOT THE ONLY ONE.
OUR LORD IS THE ONLY ONE TO EVER DEFEAT DEATH...
gag
...BUT THE NURSES AT BETHEL PRESBYTERIAN SURE ARE THE NEXT BEST THING, AREN'T THEY?
WE PROTECT EACH OTHER IN THIS TOWN.
SINNERS AND SAINTS ALIKE.
I GOTTA GO.

WHAT HE DID TO HIS DAUGHTER
CAN'T BELIEV PASTOR STEPH KEEPS IT UP.
HAVE SOME WRAPS
ILABLE UP FRONT IF
WORKING TOGETHER IS WHAT KEEPS THIS TOWN STRONG
EXCUSE ME.
Ah. IT'S YOU.
HONORA
SERVI
30 YEA
THOMAS 'RED' THOMPSON
JEREMIAH LAWSON
OLIVER McDEVITT
AND DOESN'T EVERYONE DESERVE SALVATION IN THE END?
SEE YOU SHRUGGING, BROTHER EDISON.
STEP INTO MY OFFICE.
GIVE IT UP to THE LORD
EXIT

YOU WANT ONE?
NO, 'COURSE YOU DON'T.
STUPID QUESTION.
TSST
OLD STYLE
ARE YOU OKAY?
Heh.
SAY...
'R YOU WEARING MY CLOTHES?
Oh! YEAH. I'M SORRY. TABBY SAID IT WAS OKAY.
I-I WAS LOOKING FOR HER AFTER LAST NIGHT, AND SHE WAS AT YOUR uh, SHACK, AND...
'S FINE.
THAT BAND SUCKS ANYWAY.
I-ISN'T THIS YOUR BAND?
YEAH. AND THEY SUCK.
Y'KNOW I WROTE ALL THEIR SONGS? EVERY HOOK.
I GOT US EVERY GIG. PLAYED LEAD GUITAR.
WAS ME EVERYONE WAS THERE TO SEE.
AND THEN THEY F-FUCKIN' DROPPED ME.
AN' IT WAS FOR NOTHING. THEY DI'N'T EVEN KEEP TOURING.
ANYWAY. THINGS ARE LOOKING UP.
GOT SOME SHITTY JANITORIAL JOB IN MY SHITTY LITTLE HOMETOWN.
WHERE I CAN'T EVEN DO MY SHITTY JOB BECAUSE PEOPLE ARE STEALING PAINT FROM THE CHURCH FOR SOME SHITTY REASON.
BUT HEY...

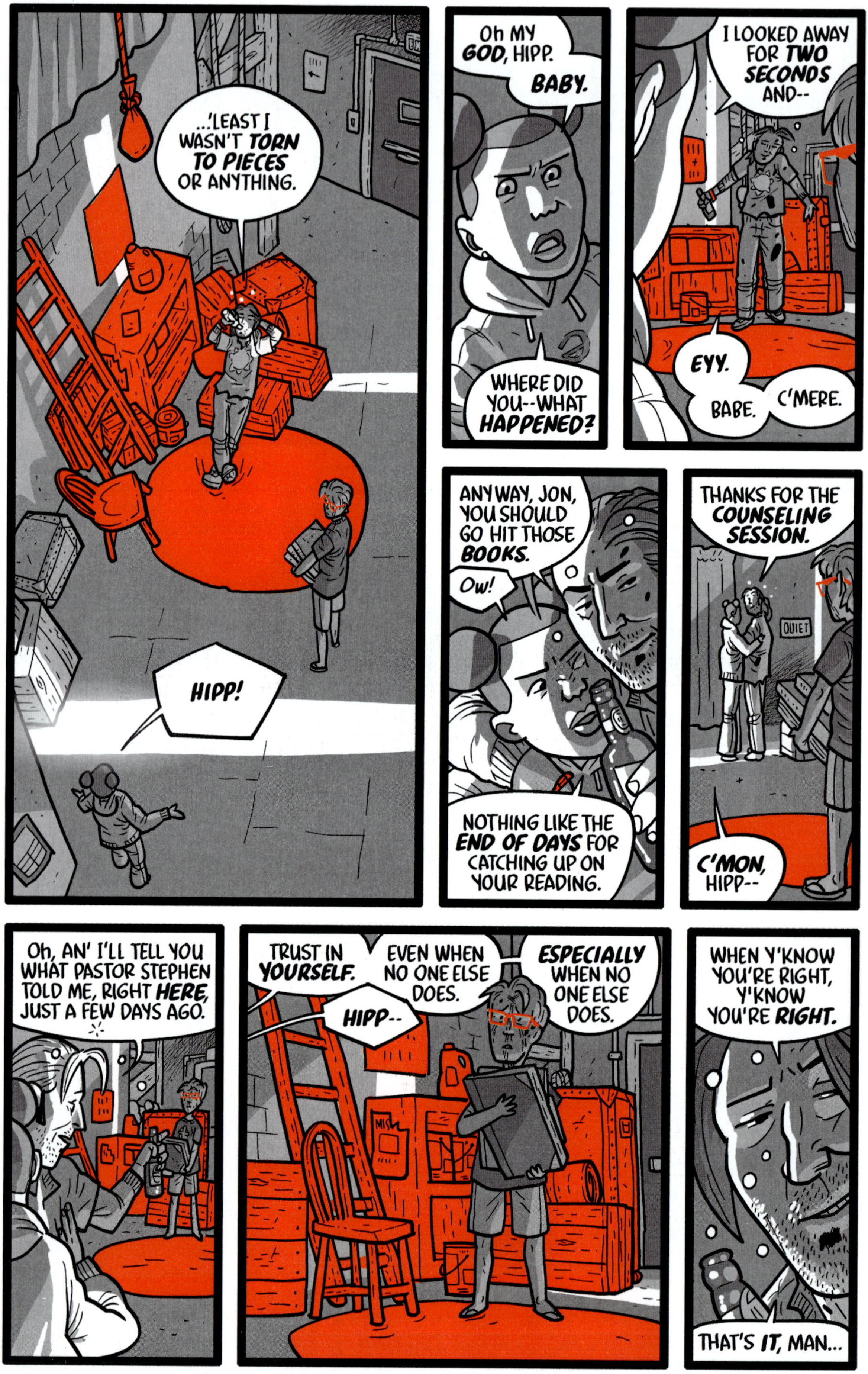
...'LEAST I WASN'T TORN TO PIECES OR ANYTHING.
HIPP!
Oh MY GOD, HIPP.
BABY.
WHERE DID YOU--WHAT HAPPENED?
I LOOKED AWAY FOR TWO SECONDS AND--
EYY.
BABE.
C'MERE.
ANYWAY, JON, YOU SHOULD GO HIT THOSE BOOKS.
Ow!
NOTHING LIKE THE END OF DAYS FOR CATCHING UP ON YOUR READING.
THANKS FOR THE COUNSELING SESSION.
QUIET
C'MON, HIPP--
Oh, AN' I'LL TELL YOU WHAT PASTOR STEPHEN TOLD ME, RIGHT HERE, JUST A FEW DAYS AGO.
TRUST IN YOURSELF.
HIPP--
EVEN WHEN NO ONE ELSE DOES.
ESPECIALLY WHEN NO ONE ELSE DOES.
WHEN Y'KNOW YOU'RE RIGHT, Y'KNOW YOU'RE RIGHT.
THAT'S IT, MAN...

"...THAT'S WHAT FAITH IS."
sniff
PLEASE.
JUST... PLEASE.
T-TAKE THIS POISON OUT OF ME.
JON?
TABBY, I--
ARE YOU OKAY?
sniff I'M OKAY.
DID, uh, DID YOU FIND SOMETHING?
...NO.
I-I DIDN'T. I COULDN'T.

THEN LET'S FUCKING GO.
SLAM
KCHIK
WE'LL GET YOU OUT OF TOWN.
FIFTY MILES, MAYBE.
WE CAN AT LEAST MAKE THAT SON OF A BITCH **WORK** FOR IT.
VRRRN

HONK
I THINK HERE'S GOOD.
YEAH. HERE'S GOOD.
HISTORICAL SITE
END of CHAPTER FOUR

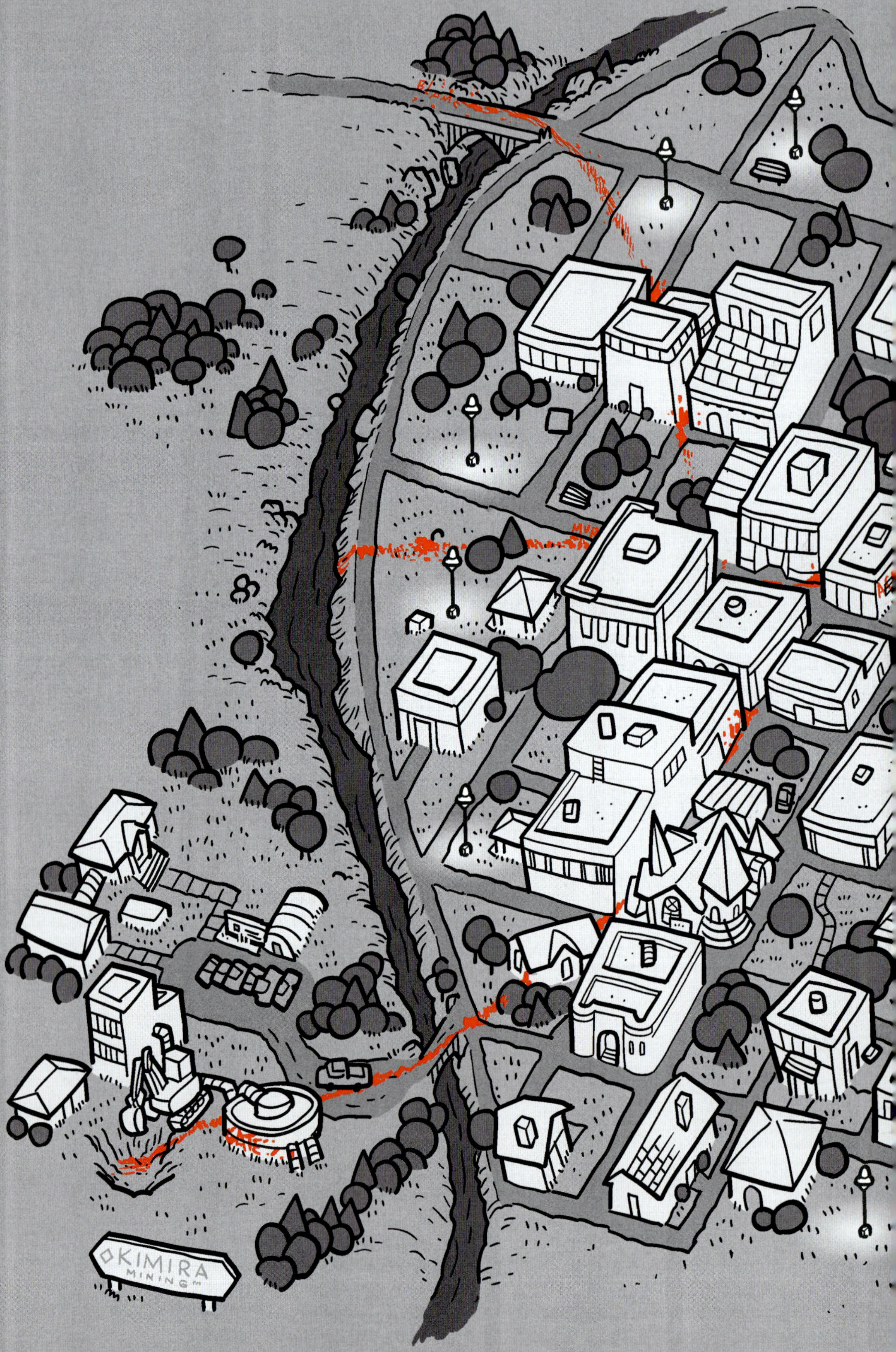
KIMIRA
MINING™

FIVE

MILE
182

GO TIGERS!
FIRE
MATH 206
NICOLI
WRES
196

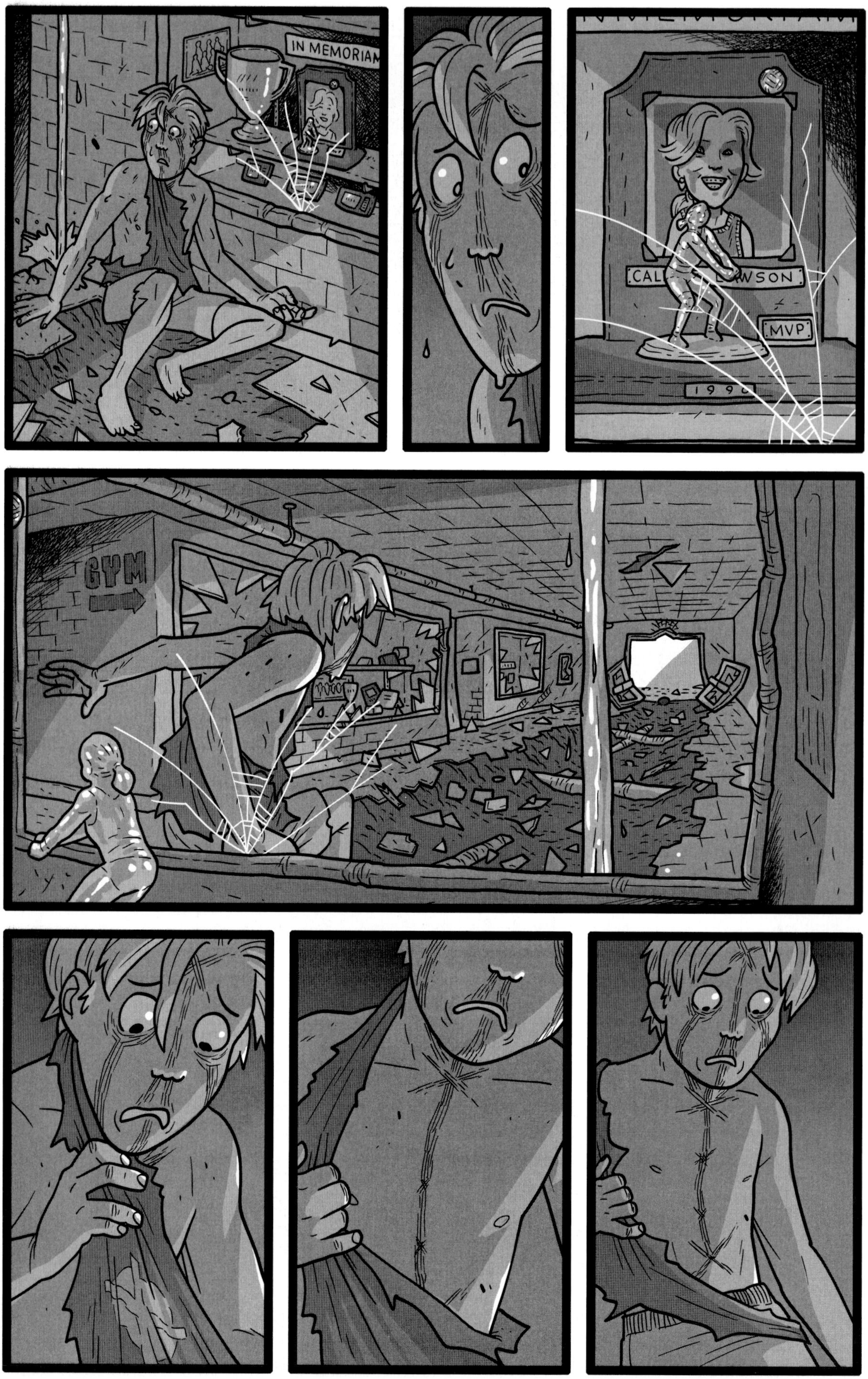
IN MEMORIAM
MVP
GYM

WRESTLINGCHAMPS
1966
EXIT
JOSIAH
TIGERS
VISITOR
PERIOD
MATCH

FIRE
GYM
EXIT
DARE
I HAVE YOUR GLASSES.
THANK--
THANK YOU.
SIN
TABBY...
DID IT WORK?
I-I THINK IT WORKED.
I MEAN, THERE'S A LOT OF BROKEN STUFF BACK THERE, BUT, Y'KNOW--
JON...
JESUS.

TURKEY
MISSING
MISSING

THURSDAY

Oh MY GOD
JESUS--
NO, NO, NO--
SCHOOL
WHY IS THIS HAPPENING TO ME?
I'M JUST TRYING TO BE G-GOOD.
TABBY, IT'S IMPOSSIBLE. IT'S JUST--
SMACK
CLATTER
IT'S HAPPENING TO ALL OF US.
NOW. IT'S BEEN A LONG NIGHT.
LET'S GO.

SPISH
BDEEP
ENTIFICATION
TABITHA STEVENS
KTANK
SHAKE
OKAY, LET'S GET UP TO THE *LAB.*
I'VE GOT SOMETHING DRY FOR YOU TO WEAR.
TABBY...
TABBY, I'M SORRY I *LOST* IT. I-I'M JUST--
YOU'RE MY BEST FRIEND.
YOU CAN'T GIVE UP.

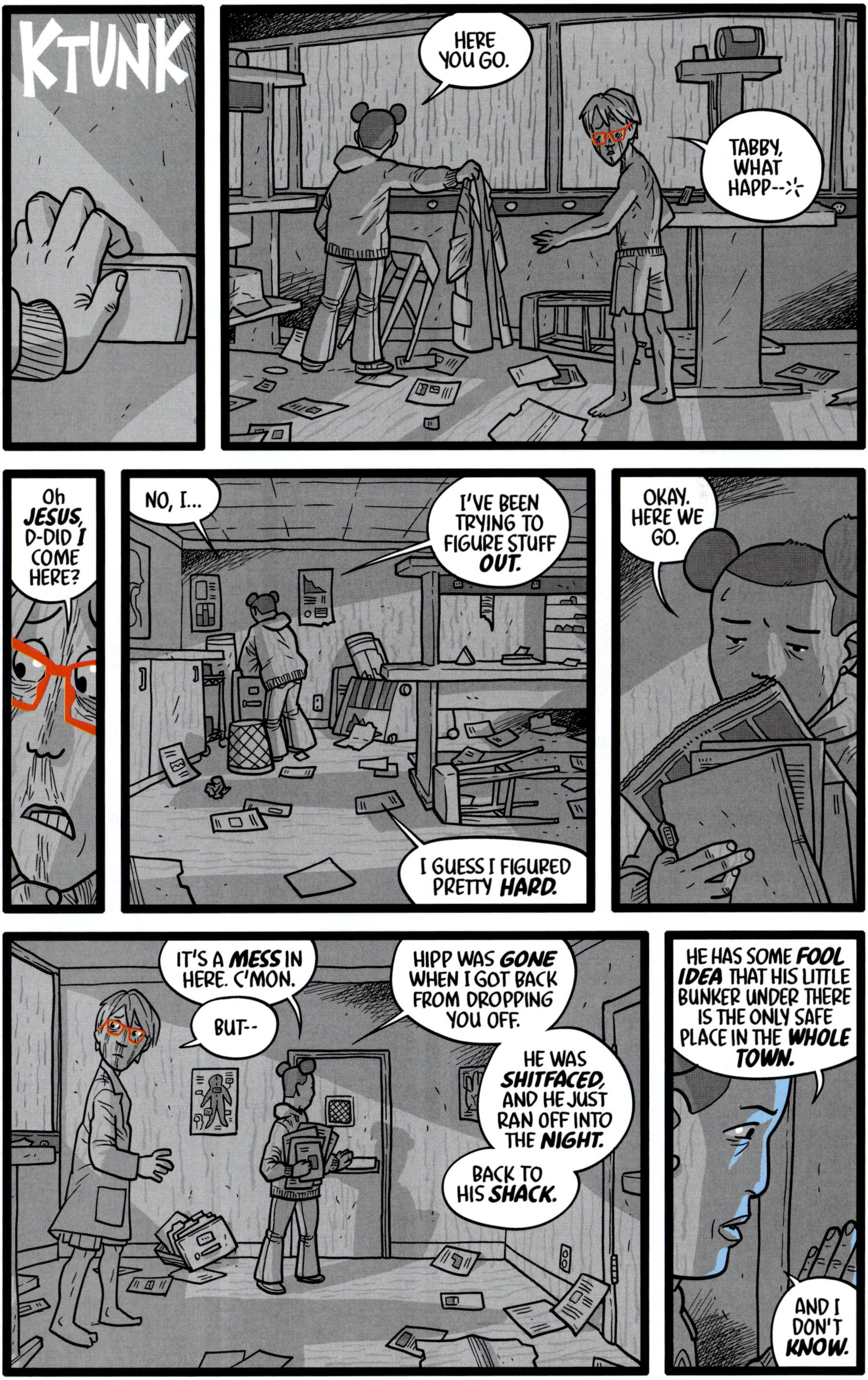
KTUNK
HERE YOU GO.
TABBY, WHAT HAPP--
Oh JESUS, D-DID I COME HERE?
NO, I...
I'VE BEEN TRYING TO FIGURE STUFF OUT.
I GUESS I FIGURED PRETTY HARD.
OKAY. HERE WE GO.
IT'S A MESS IN HERE. C'MON.
BUT--
HIPP WAS GONE WHEN I GOT BACK FROM DROPPING YOU OFF.
HE WAS SHITFACED, AND HE JUST RAN OFF INTO THE NIGHT.
BACK TO HIS SHACK.
HE HAS SOME FOOL IDEA THAT HIS LITTLE BUNKER UNDER THERE IS THE ONLY SAFE PLACE IN THE WHOLE TOWN.
AND I DON'T KNOW.

MAYBE HE'S RIGHT.
OKAY. THIS IS WHAT I'VE GOT.
WE'VE BEEN TRYING TO TRAP THIS THING, RIGHT? BUT THAT DOESN'T WORK. I THINK WE'RE THINKING ABOUT IT WRONG.
I THINK WE NEED TO WEAKEN IT.
WEAKEN IT?
YEAH. THERE'S GOT TO BE SOMETHING, RIGHT?
SOMETHING THAT MAKES IT WEAKER. VULNERABLE.

WELL, I KNOW WHAT MAKES IT STRONG.
WHAT?
APPARENTLY ANYTHING I DO TO AVOID HURTING PEOPLE.
EVERY TIME I TRY TO BE GOOD, IT'S LIKE STEROIDS FOR EVIL ENTITIES OR WHATEVER.
OKAY. I KNOW THAT'S WHERE YOU'VE LANDED ON THIS, BUT JUST...
JUST LOOK HERE.
LAST WEEK, BEFORE ANY OF THIS HAPPENED...
JOSIAH TRI
Thursday, June 2, 1996
Josiah, IA
GRIM ANNIVERSARY
Collapse at Kimir
by Ben Smith
DISASTER CLAIMS THREE LIVES
...THERE WAS A COLLAPSE AT THE MINE.
THE COMPANY THAT RUNS IT, I GUESS THEY GOT TO THE NEWSPAPER AND SO THE ARTICLE MOSTLY JUST READS LIKE IT WAS A REGULAR ACCIDENT.
EXCEPT FOR THIS ONE LINE.
words just after t
Curran. "The
below us," Curran s
"The smell was
absolutely unbearabl
veryone started
omiting and no one
ould move." A Kimira
presentative quickl
ved in, which stopp
rran from goi
THE COMPANY HAD THAT SECTION OF THE MINE SEALED UP BY SUNDAY MORNING.
BUT I THINK SOMETHING GOT OUT.
AN INFECTION.
TABBY, I TOLD YOU, IT'S NOT--
OKAY, OKAY, BUT THAT'S NOT WHAT'S IMPORTANT.

UNTIL THE ACCIDENT, IT WAS CONTAINED.
THAT MEANS THERE'S SOMETHING IN THE MINE THAT WEAKENS IT.
Oh, WOW.
EXACTLY.
COPPER.
IRON.
IRON IS DEADLY TO EVIL CREATURES. THAT MAKES PERFECT SENSE.
NO, JON, COPPER. IT'S A NATURAL ANTIBACTERIAL SUBSTANCE THAT--
Y'KNOW WHAT? WE'RE SAYING THE SAME THING HERE.
WE HAVE TO GET YOU TO THAT MINE.
IF WE CAN GET YOU DOWN INTO THAT SEALED AREA AND CLOSE IT OFF, WE CAN CONTAIN THIS THING.
DON'T YOU THINK?
O-OKAY, SURE, BUT...
...LIKE...
...THEN WHAT?
KTUNK

MISS STEVENS!
WHAT ARE YOU DOING HERE?
EVERYONE'S SUPPOSED TO BE OUT OF THE BUILDING UNTIL THE ALL CLEAR.
I KNOW, SIR, I--
I'M JUST PICKING UP THE LAST COUPLE THINGS.
AND WHO'S THIS GUY?
KRIK IK IK
HE'S DEFINITELY NOT S'POSED TO BE HERE.
THIS IS MY FRIEND JON. I THINK I'VE MENTIONED--
Uh...
KRIK IK IK IK
RIGHT. RIGHT RIGHT.
KRIK IK IK
GOT IT. GOT IT.
OKAY, WELL, WE'RE GOING TO uh, LOCK THIS PLACE DOWN FOR THE BIG SWEEP, SO FINISH UP QUICK.
KRIK IK IK IK
KTUNK

YOU READY TO GO?
IT'S GOING TO TAKE US A WHILE TO WALK THERE.
KLOP KLOP
WE'RE NOT GOING TO TAKE YOUR CAR? IT'S RAINING PRETTY HARD.
NO, 'FRAID NOT. I PARKED IN THE WRONG PLACE.
WHAT? WHERE?
WELL, JONATHAN, BETWEEN YOU...
...AND WHEREVER YOU WERE GOING.
KCHAK
SSSHHHHHHHHHH

SSHHHHHHHHHHHHH
SHHHHHHHHHHHHHHHH
D'YOU WANT TO GO BY YOUR HOUSE?
BRING SOME FOOD OR SOMETHING?
NO--
NO, IT'S OKAY.
I'M NOT HUNGRY AT ALL.

KIM
MINING CO
OKAY, HOLD UP, HOLD UP.
HUHH
HUHH
I JUST NEED TO REST FOR A SECOND.
HUHH HUHH
YOU OKAY?
HUHH
HUHH
YEAH, I...
HUHH
HUHH
H-H-H HUHH
Oh, HEY...
H-H-HUHH
I'M A MURDERER.
PASSES
LISTEN, YOU'RE NOT--
HUHH
I AM.
I AM.
HOW COULD I NOT BE?
OKAY, WELL, LISTEN, uh...
I-I-I DON'T KNOW IF IT MAKES YOU FEEL ANY BETTER, BUT...
...Y'KNOW, HIPP HAS A THEORY ABOUT IT.
HIPP DOES?
YEAH, Y'KNOW, IT'S LIKE, uh...

HE SAYS **GOD** IS CLEANSING THE EARTH.
LIKE, uh, SMITING THE **UNWORTHY.**
SPARING THE INNOCENT.
LEAVING THE **RIGHTEOUS** TO RULE IN THE AFTERMATH.
JESUS.
THAT'S NOT COMFORTING **AT ALL.**
JUST...THINNING OUT THE **HERD?**
I-IS THAT HOW HE SEES **GOD?**
I DUNNO.
HE WAS PRETTY **DRUNK** WHEN HE SAID IT.
Oh, BUT HE SAID THE **REASON** IS BECAUSE THIS TOWN **SUCKS.**
HMPP!
SORRY.
I KNOW. IT WASN'T THAT FUNNY AT THE **TIME**, BUT...
HUH.
SSHHHHHHHH
HA HA HA HA HA HA
HA HA HA HA HA HA
OKAY.
C'MON, LET'S GO.

I GOT THE MAP OF THE MINE.
SO THE CHAMBER WE WANT IS DEEP INSIDE, ah... THAT TUNNEL THERE.
THAT--
Oh.
OH.
TABBY...
CAN I ASK YOU A FAVOR?
WHAT?
YEAH, OF COURSE.
IT'S JUST...THIS IS A PLACE I, uh, WAS AT BEFORE.
IT'S REALLY BAD, AND...
C-CAN YOU CLOSE YOUR EYES FOR THIS PART?
JON...
I'M JUST GOING TO SEE IT ANYWAY WHEN I COME BACK UP.

I KNOW.
JUST...PLEASE.
I-I CAN'T BEAR TO HAVE YOU LOOK AT ME THAT WAY.
OKAY.
TH-THIS WAY. BIG STEP.
OVER TO YOUR RIGHT.
STRAIGHT.

OKAY, YOU CAN OPEN 'EM.
DO NOT ENTER
RIP
NNF
OKAY.
CHKCHAK
KLIK
OKAY.
VRNNNN

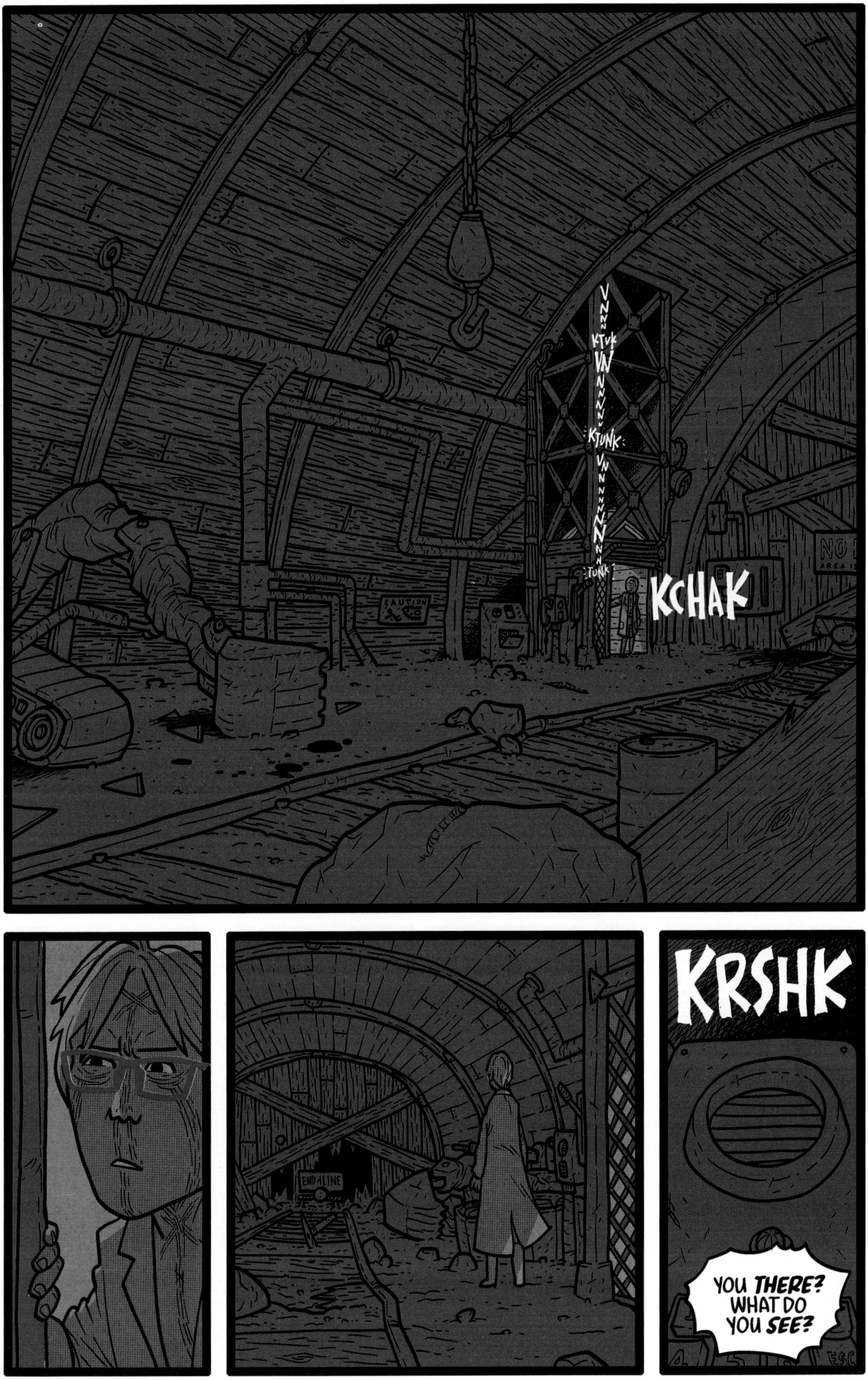
VNNN
KTUK
VNNNNNN
KTUNK
VNNNNNNNNN
TUNK
KCHAK
CAUTION
END OF LINE
KRSHK
YOU *THERE?* WHAT DO YOU *SEE?*

IT'S REALLY DARK.
I CAN HARDLY SEE ANYTHING.
DO YOU--
OW!
NNF
DO YOU THINK THIS IS GOING TO WORK?
I...I DON'T KNOW.
IT SEEMS LIKE IT, BUT...
COME ON, TABBY.
YOU'RE THE SMARTEST PERSON I KNOW.
sniff
THEN YEAH.
IT'S GONNA WORK.
YEAH.
IT'S GONNA WORK.
STILL.
GET SOMEWHERE SAFE, OKAY?
OKAY.
OVER AND OUT.
END OF CHAPTER FIVE

KIMIRA
MINING™

SIX

END
LINE

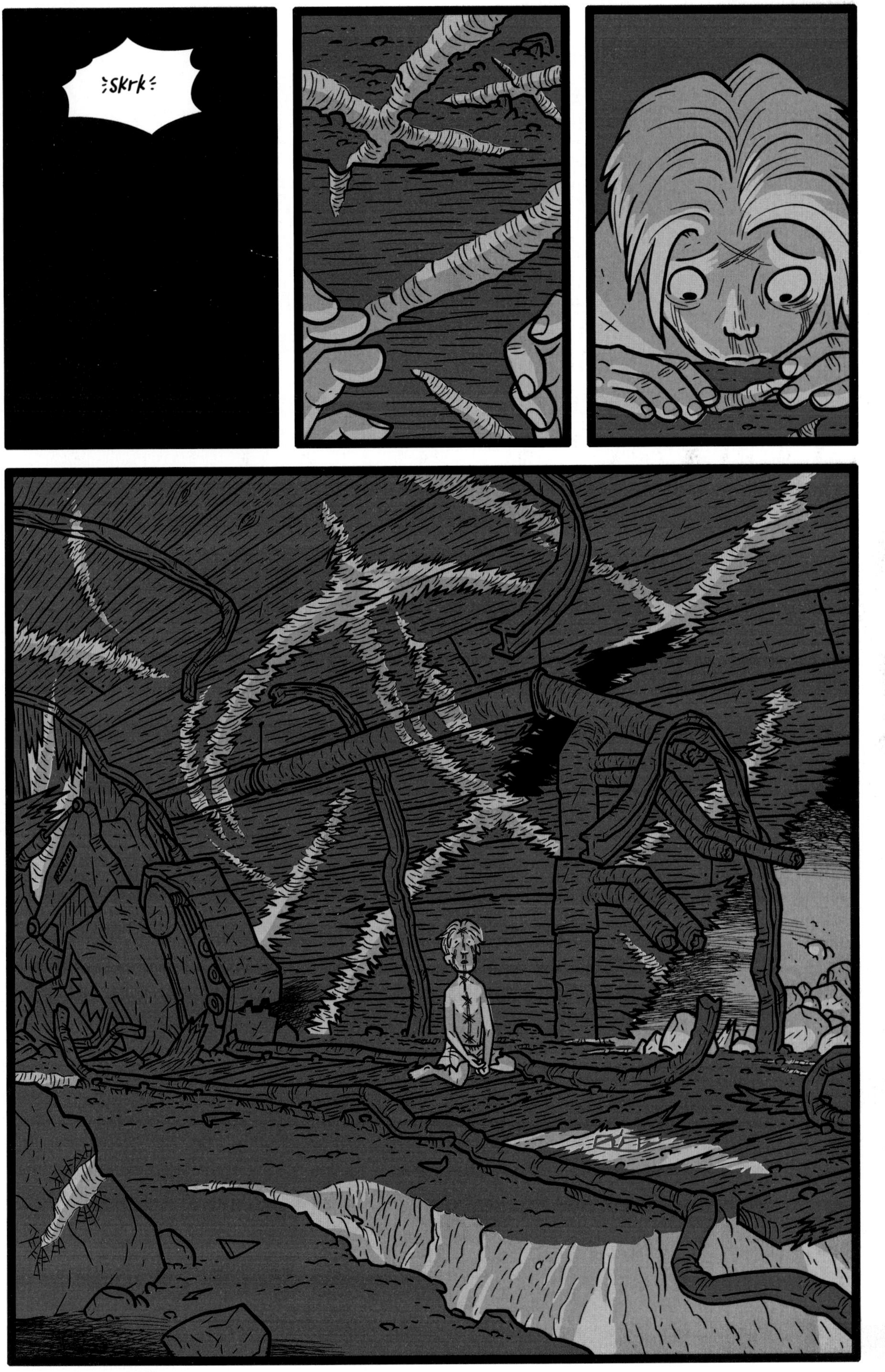
skrk

KKRK
TABBY?
TABBY? ARE YOU THERE?

SKK
TABBY, I...
I DON'T KNOW IF YOU CAN HEAR ME, BUT I-I THINK...
I THINK IT WORKED.
AND NOT JUST THAT. LIKE, IT'S A DISASTER DOWN HERE.
THE-- THE THING JUST TORE THE PLACE APART.
IT WAS ALREADY A WRECK, BUT.. WOW.
I THINK LOCKING ME DOWN HERE...
Y'KNOW, TRYING TO STOP IT...
...L-LIKE, DOING SOMETHING GOOD...
I THINK THAT REALLY PISSED IT OFF.
A-AND THIS IS ALL THANKS TO YOU.
YOU FIGURED IT OUT.
YOU DIDN'T GIVE UP ON ME.
LIKE, I, uh...
I REALLY APPRECIATE THAT.
SKRKK ON? SSKK OU HEAR ME? SSKK
SKKSK?E YOU STILL THERE?
DID I LOSE YOU?
JON?

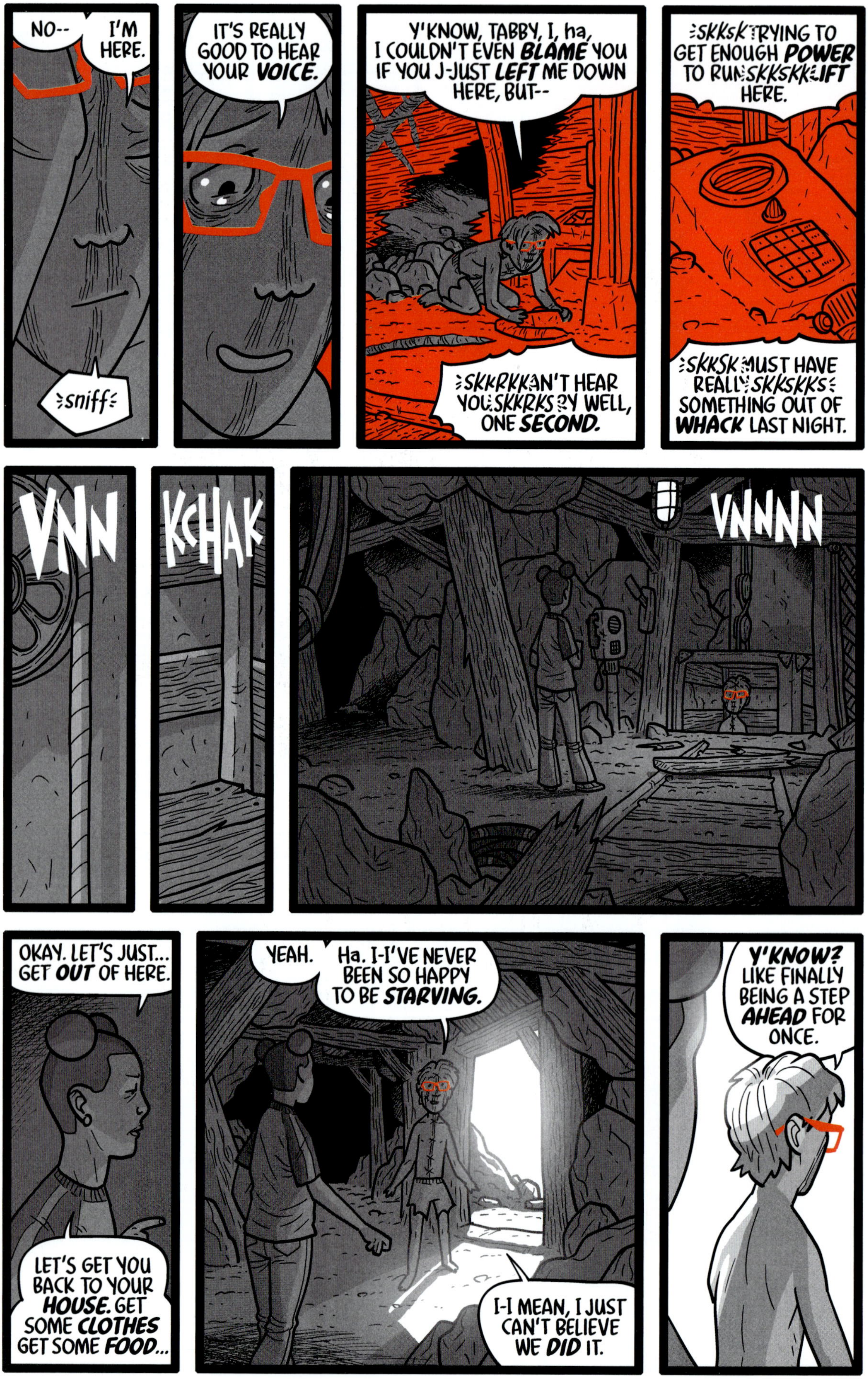

NO--
I'M HERE.
sniff
IT'S REALLY GOOD TO HEAR YOUR VOICE.
Y'KNOW, TABBY, I, ha, I COULDN'T EVEN BLAME YOU IF YOU J-JUST LEFT ME DOWN HERE, BUT--
SKKRKKAN'T HEAR YOUSKKRKSRY WELL, ONE SECOND.
SKKSKTRYING TO GET ENOUGH POWER TO RUNSKKSKKLIFT HERE.
SKKSK MUST HAVE REALLSKKSKKS SOMETHING OUT OF WHACK LAST NIGHT.
VNN
KCHAK
VNNNN
OKAY. LET'S JUST... GET OUT OF HERE.
LET'S GET YOU BACK TO YOUR HOUSE. GET SOME CLOTHES GET SOME FOOD...
YEAH.
Ha. I-I'VE NEVER BEEN SO HAPPY TO BE STARVING.
I-I MEAN, I JUST CAN'T BELIEVE WE DID IT.
Y'KNOW? LIKE FINALLY BEING A STEP AHEAD FOR ONCE.

FRIDAY

TABBY. Oh JESUS!
JESUS. WHAT HAPPENED?!
Oh MY GOD, I--
STOP. STOP IT.
IT'S FINE. IT'S OKAY.
IT'S NOT OKAY. WHAT HAP-- WHO DID THIS TO YOU?
DID...
DID HIPP DO THIS TO YOU?
LISTEN, IT'S...
HE WAS DRUNK, AGAIN.
HE WOULDN'T LET ME IN THE BUNKER. I'D ALREADY WALKED A LONG WAY THERE...
...SO I GUESS I STARTED TALKING SOME SHIT.
ANYWAY.
LET'S GET YOU HOME.
WE GOT STUFF TO TAKE CARE OF.
AND DON'T WORRY.
I DIDN'T TELL HIM YOUR DEAL.
MY..? JESUS, WHO CARES ABOUT--
MISS STEVENS!

SHOVE
HEY, I THOUGHT I SAW YOU OVER THERE!
OKAY, SO WE'VE ALMOST COMPLETED THIS SWEEP.
TABBY, WHAT--
SHH.
LIKE, I DIDN'T KNOW YOU WERE ASSIGNED TO THIS QUADRANT.
ANYWAY, THE READINGS ARE HOT OFF THIS PAINT-- NO SURPRISE THERE -- BUT WE'RE SEEING A TON FROM CERTAIN PIECES OF MINING EQUIPMENT.
Uh, OKAY.
KRIK IK IK
ALL OVER THE TOWN, TOO. PARTS OF THE POLICE STATION MADE THIS GIZMO GO NUTS.
HONESTLY, I DON'T KNOW WHAT ALL THIS IS ABOUT, BUT IT SOUNDS LIKE PHILLIPS IS TALKING TO THE CHIEF ABOUT A THEORY.
KRIK IK IK
LIKE, IN ADDITION TO CATCHING THIS THING, THEY MIGHT BE ABLE TO LINK IT TO AN OLD CASE.
HERE?

AND WHAT
APPENED TO
OUR FAC
SAFET

SPLASH
NNF
WHAT THE F--
SHIT!!
Oh, NO--

KOFF
HGKF
YOU.

LOOK...
...WE DON'T HAVE TO GET INTO THIS.
YOU EVIL PIECE OF SHIT.
I KNOW.
I KNOW.
I'M ALMOST DONE, YOU KNOW!
YOU CAN'T ERASE IT. PEOPLE WILL KNOW.
IT WON'T WORK!
YOU HEAR ME?!
THEY'LL SEE WHAT I SEE!!

KILLER

KRIK
IK IK
OPTICAL
DEATH

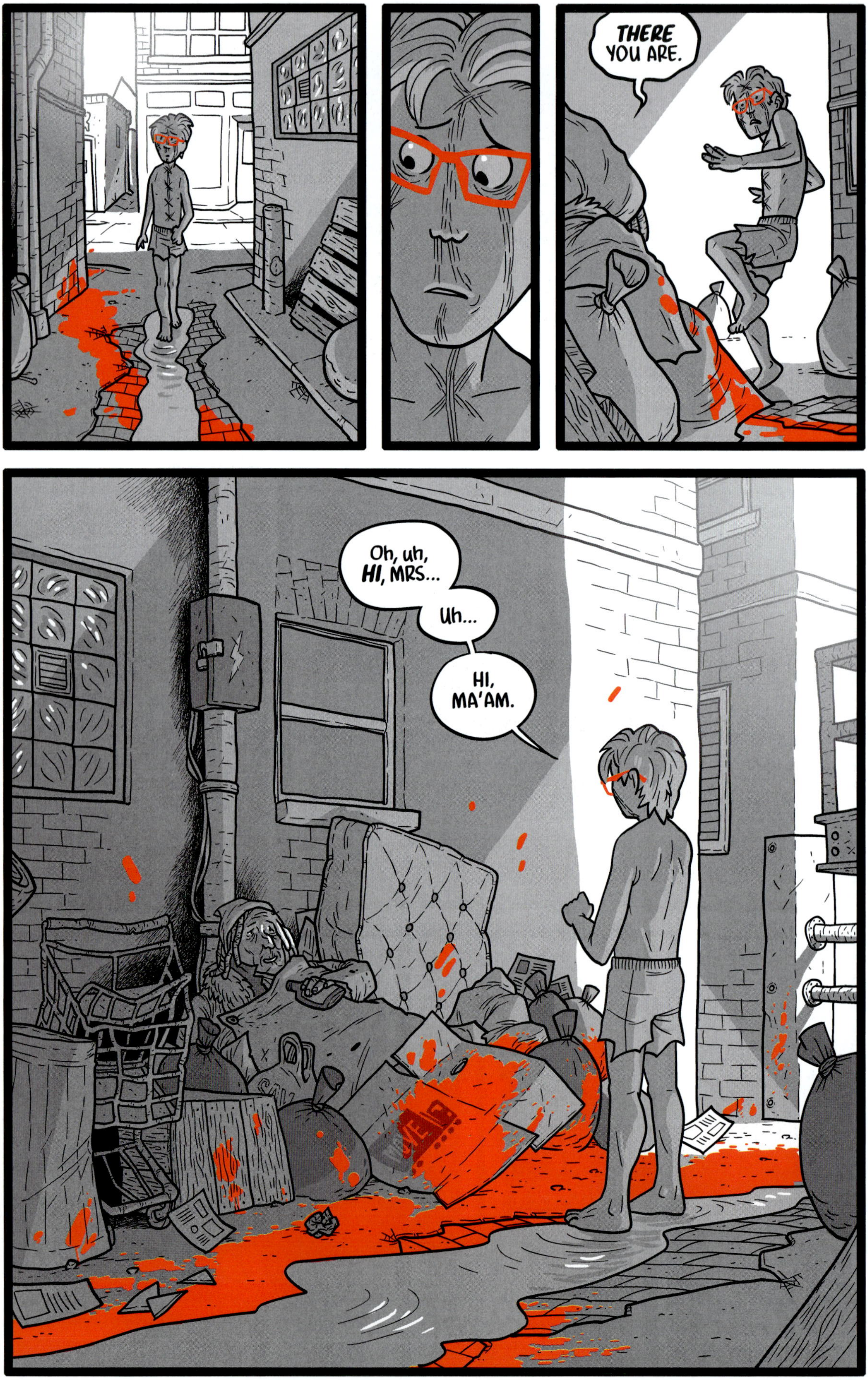
THERE YOU ARE.
Oh, uh, HI, MRS...
Uh...
HI, MA'AM.

HUH.
YOU HAVEN'T CALLED ME THAT IN A WHILE.
"MOM."
Oh, NO, WAIT, I DIDN'T--
'S REALLY NICE.
Y-YOU BEEN AT SCHOOL A LOT. LATE.
WE HARDLY EVER SEE YOU.
I MEAN, YOUR FATHER AIN'T GOOD COMPANY.
I'M Y-YELLIN' AT HIM ALLA TIME TO SOBER UP.
"JEREMIAH! Y-YA DUMB SUMBITCH!
"YA LOUSY..."
Uh, MA'AM, I GOTTA--
Uh...
THAP
I KNOW YOU GOT STUFF GOIN' ON. Y-YOU'RE SMART, Y-Y'GOT PROSPECTS.
I-I DUNNO HOW TO HELP YOU WITH THAT, BABY. BUT ALL YOU G-GOT TO DO IS ASK.
Uh, M-MA'AM, SORRY. LISTEN, I-I'M NOT THE--I'M NOT YOUR DAUGHTER. SHE--I MEAN, WE WENT TO SCHOOL TOGETHER.
I-I'M JONATHAN. I WORK AT THE COFFEE SHOP. I--
Oh COME ON NOW, HONEY. SURE YOU ARE.
YOU'RE GROWN, BUT I J-JUST GOT TO LOOK IN YOUR EYES.
STILL IN THERE.
STILL THE SAME OLD CALIE.

O-OKAY.
I-I GOTTA GO.
YOU'LL COME BACK?
YOU'LL COME BACK, WON'T YOU?
YEAH.
OKAY.
I'LL COME BACK.
HIGH SCHOOL

JOSIAH

Oh DAMN.
IT SPARED YOU, TOO.
nng
HELL YEAH. AS IT WAS FUCKING WRITTEN.
"WATCHES OVER DRUNKS AND CHILDREN."
UP TOP.
NO? 'KAY.
ANYWAY.
YOU BEEN THROUGH TOWN?
HOW'S IT LOOKING OUT THERE? THOROUGHLY FUCKED?
PRETTY SOON THERE'S NOT EVEN GOING TO BE A GRID TO BE OFF OF AROUND HERE.
NO.
SHE SOLVED IT.
TABBY.
SHE FIGURED IT OUT.
SHE SAVED THE TOWN.
AND YOU FUCKING HIT HER.

...
LOOK, MAN. SOMETIMES... PEOPLE GO CRAZY.
THEY DON'T LISTEN.
I'VE SEEN IT SO MANY TIMES.
THEIR WHOLE LIVES THEY'RE JUST BEING BLOWN AROUND BY THEIR LITTLE FEELINGS.
THEY GOTTA BE REMINDED OF THE ORDER AND THE WORK THAT HOLDS EVERYTHING TOGETHER.
THERE'S SOMETHING GOING ON AROUND HERE THAT'S BEYOND HUMAN UNDERSTANDING.
I KNOW YOU AND I AGREE ON THAT.
BUT SHE THINKS SHE CAN OUT-THINK IT.
OUT-THINK GOD.
JON, THIS IS HOW THE WORLD SORTS ITSELF OUT.
SOME SURVIVE IT. OTHERS DON'T. AND YOU KNOW WHAT?
THE WORLD IMPROVES.
IF THEY DON'T ADAPT...
WE'RE BETTER OFF WITHOUT 'EM.
SHE'S MY BEST FRIEND.
SHE'S ONLY EVER HELPED PEOPLE.
AND YOU...
...HIT HER.
OKAY.
I GET IT NOW.
YOU'RE THE DEVIL.

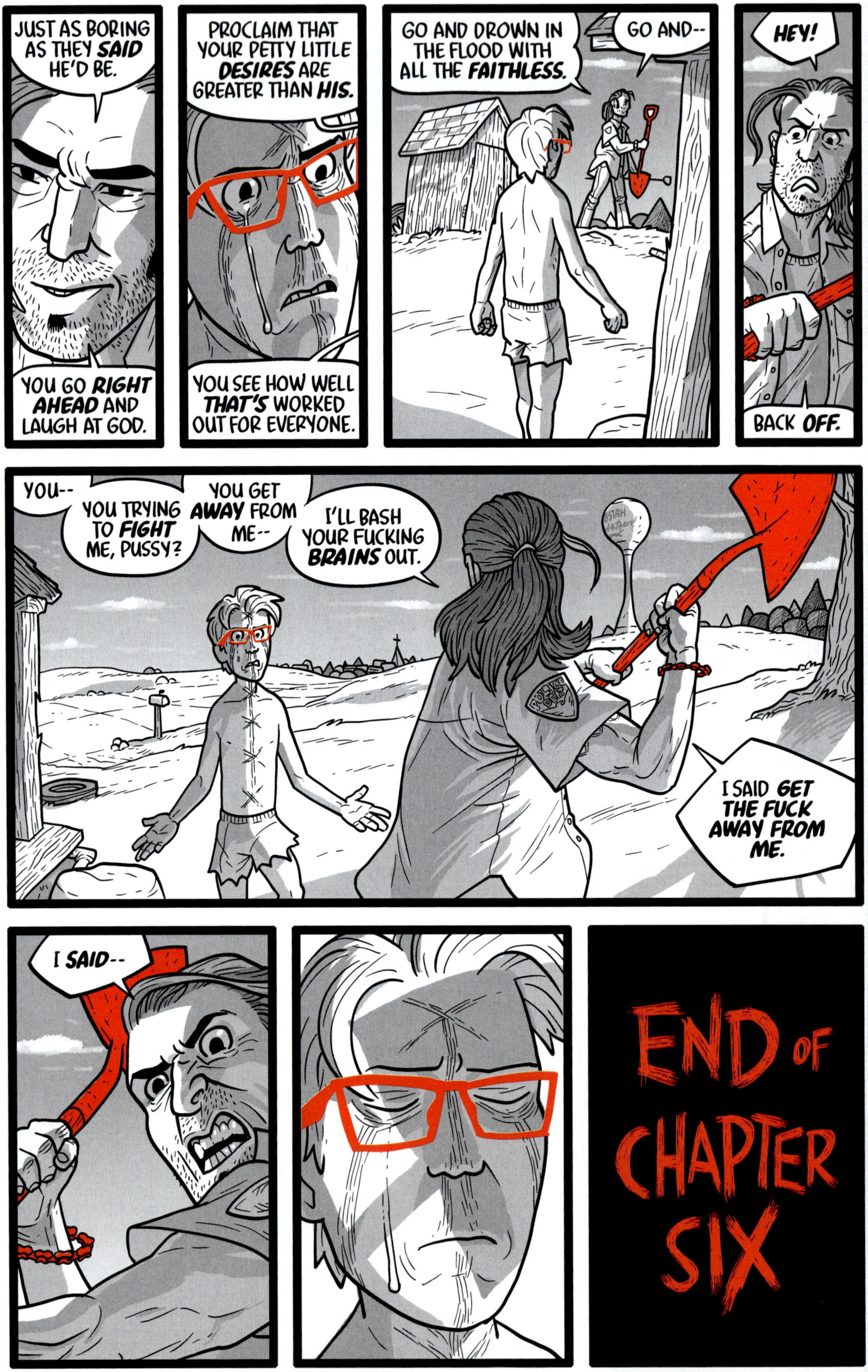
JUST AS BORING AS THEY SAID HE'D BE.
YOU GO RIGHT AHEAD AND LAUGH AT GOD.
PROCLAIM THAT YOUR PETTY LITTLE DESIRES ARE GREATER THAN HIS.
YOU SEE HOW WELL THAT'S WORKED OUT FOR EVERYONE.
GO AND DROWN IN THE FLOOD WITH ALL THE FAITHLESS.
GO AND--
HEY!
BACK OFF.
YOU--
YOU TRYING TO FIGHT ME, PUSSY?
YOU GET AWAY FROM ME--
I'LL BASH YOUR FUCKING BRAINS OUT.
I SAID GET THE FUCK AWAY FROM ME.
I SAID--
END OF CHAPTER SIX

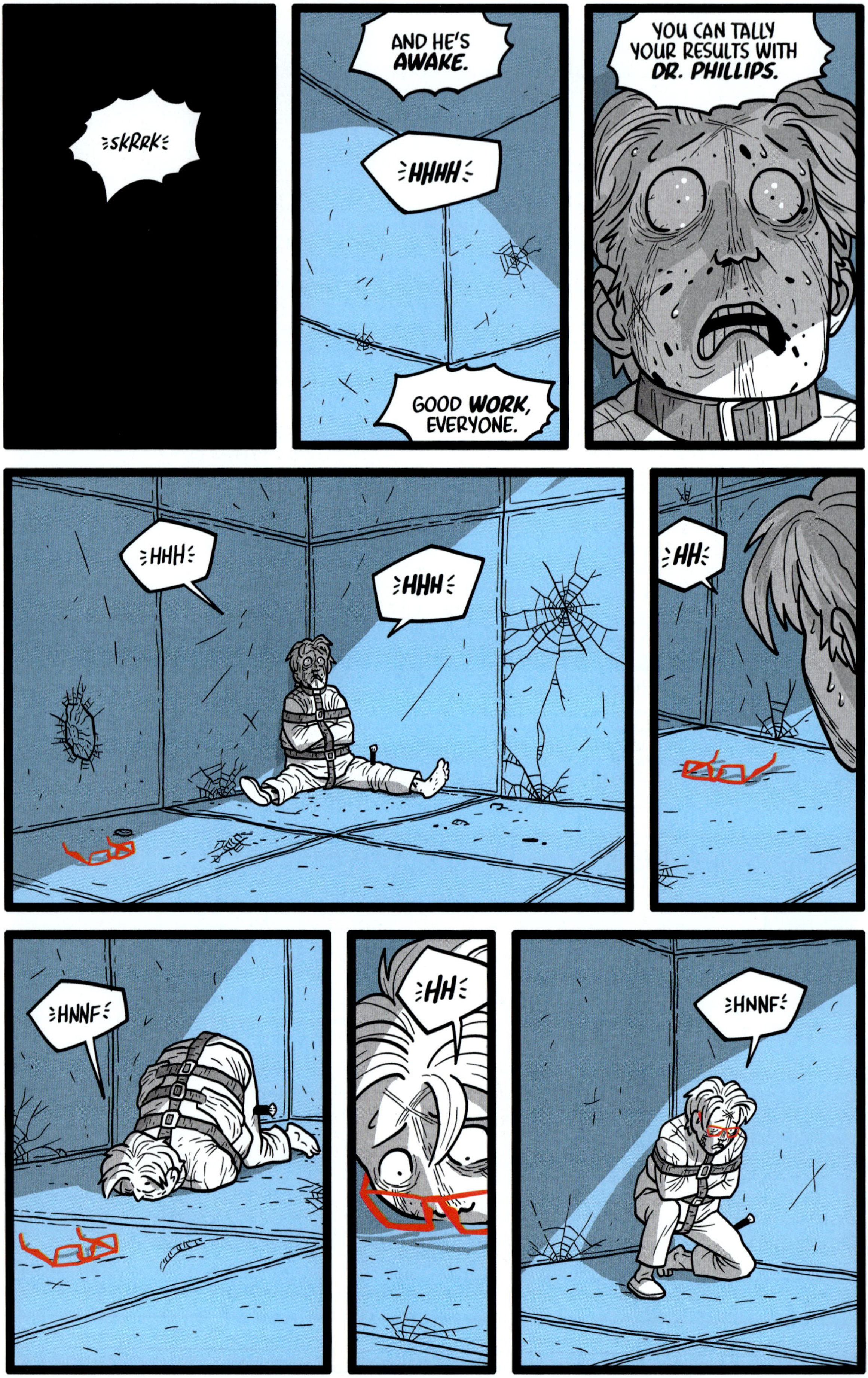

SKRRK
AND HE'S AWAKE.
HHHH
GOOD WORK, EVERYONE.
YOU CAN TALLY YOUR RESULTS WITH DR. PHILLIPS.
HHH
HHH
HH
HNNF
HH
HNNF

UNKNOWN DAY

BOLTING DOORS.
PREPARING TO POWER DOWN ULTRAVIOLET LAMPS.
FIVE.
FOUR.
EPIALOS
THREE.
EPIALOS
WHY
TWO.
ONE.
THOK
END OF CHAPTER SEVEN

SEVEN

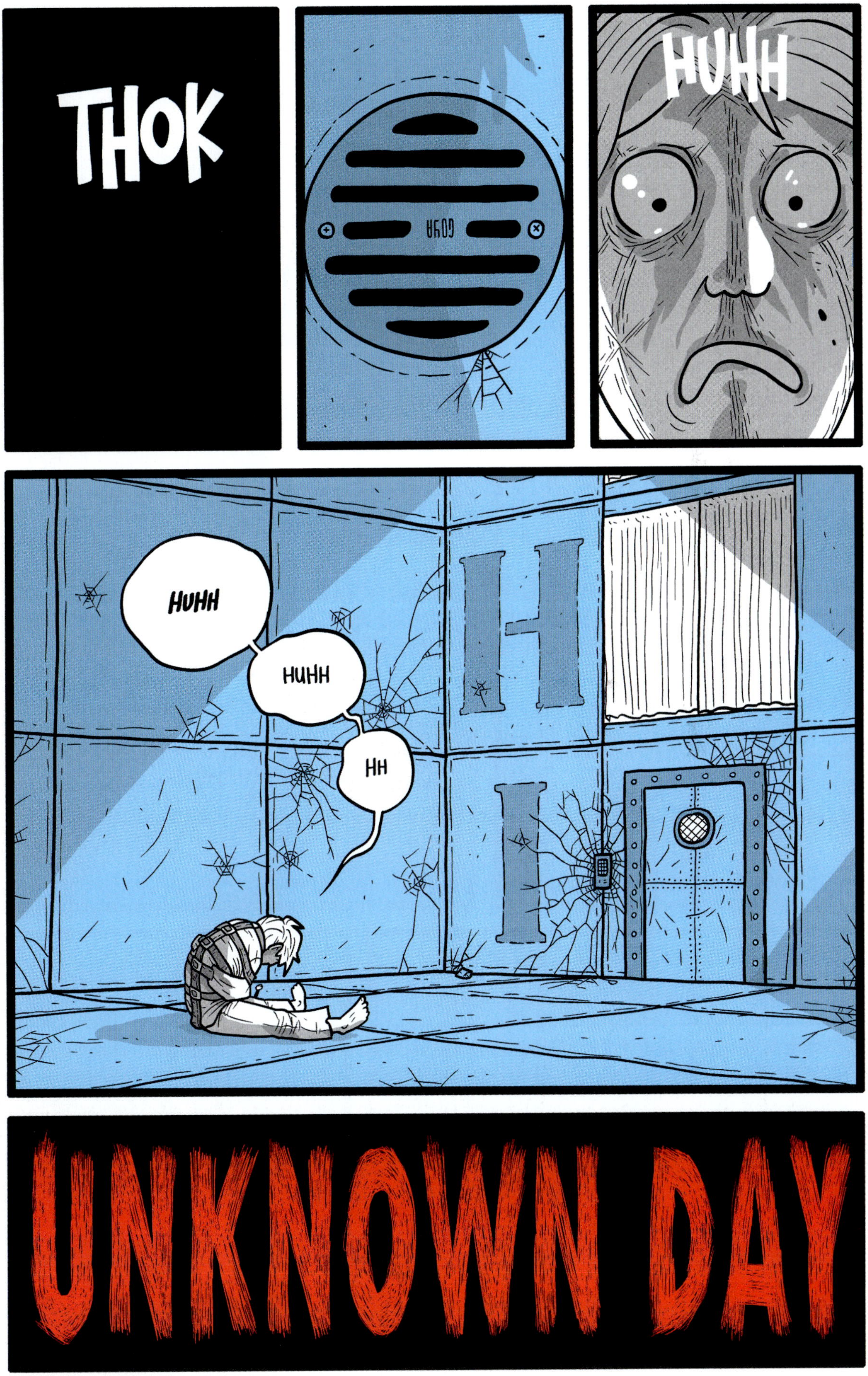
THOK
GOYA
HUHH
HUHH
HUHH
HH
UNKNOWN DAY

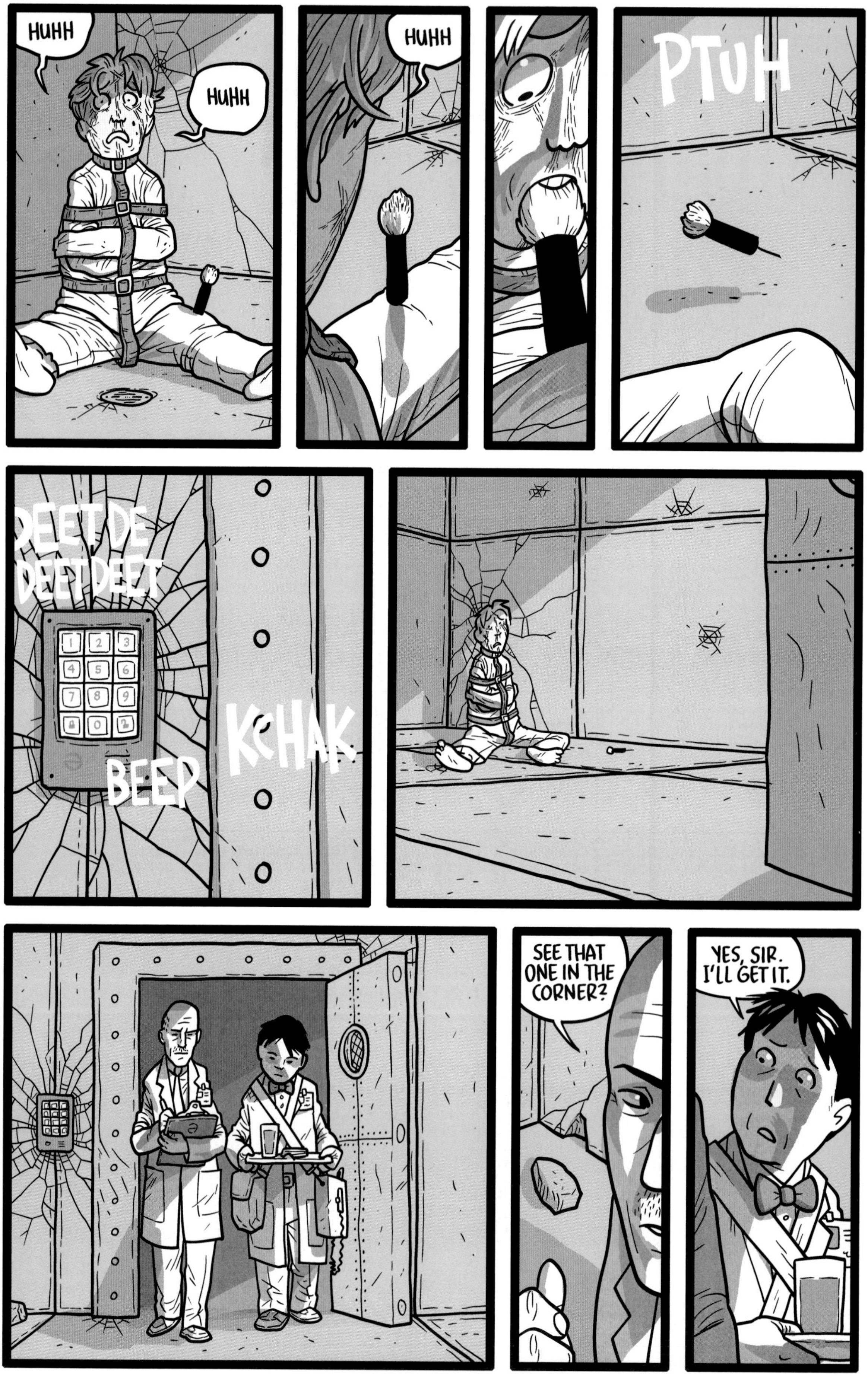
HUHH
HUHH
HUHH
PTUH
DEET DE
DEET DEET
BEEP
KCHAK
SEE THAT ONE IN THE CORNER?
YES, SIR. I'LL GET IT.

WHO--
WHAT--
TWO OVER THERE.
GOT 'EM.
WHERE'S TABBY?
PLEASE. WHERE IS--
HEY!
JACKET'S UNCOMPROMISED.
SOME FABRIC RIPS. NO STRAP DAMAGE.
GOOD. KEEP IT.
YOU BETTER EAT.
TRAY'S GOING OUT WITH US.
I KNOW YOU'RE HUNGRY.
HOMP FNF GMP

FIVE TOTAL. ALL BETWEEN FOUR AND SIX CENTIMETERS.
NMF
SCRF
NOTHING ON THE SCANNER THOUGH.
KRIK IK IK
IT'S JUST THE GLASSES.
Oh.
HOLD ON.
GULP
KLUNK
OKAY.
LOCK IT DOWN.
PLEASE. ARE YOU IN CHARGE?
WHERE'S TABBY? CAN I TALK TO--
PLEASE!

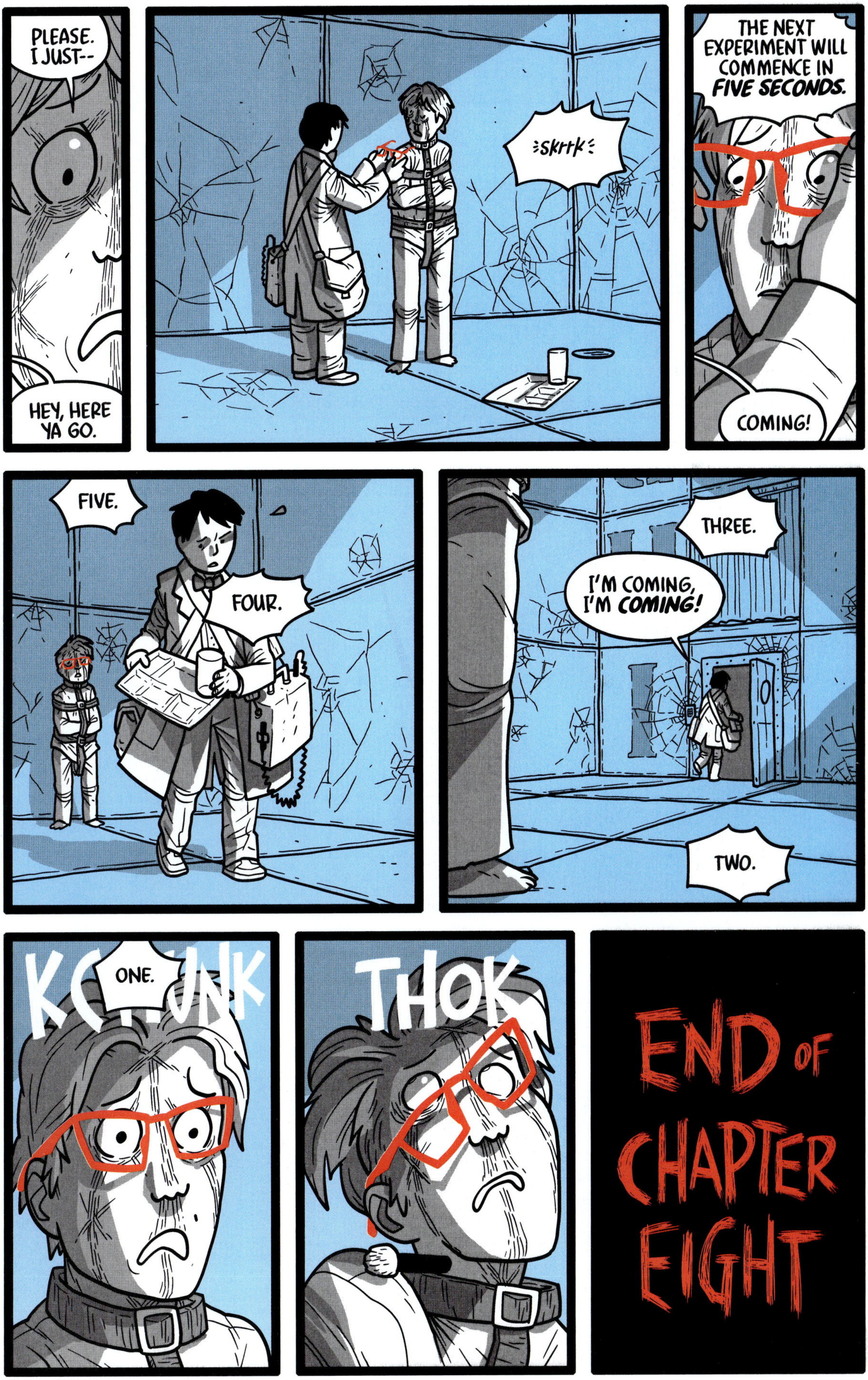
PLEASE. I JUST--
HEY, HERE YA GO.
SKRRK
THE NEXT EXPERIMENT WILL COMMENCE IN FIVE SECONDS.
COMING!
FIVE.
FOUR.
THREE.
I'M COMING, I'M COMING!
TWO.
KCHUNK
ONE.
THOK
END OF CHAPTER EIGHT

THOK
HUHH
KLAK
GULP
skrrk
PLEASE--
PLE--
THOK
END OF CHAPTER NINE

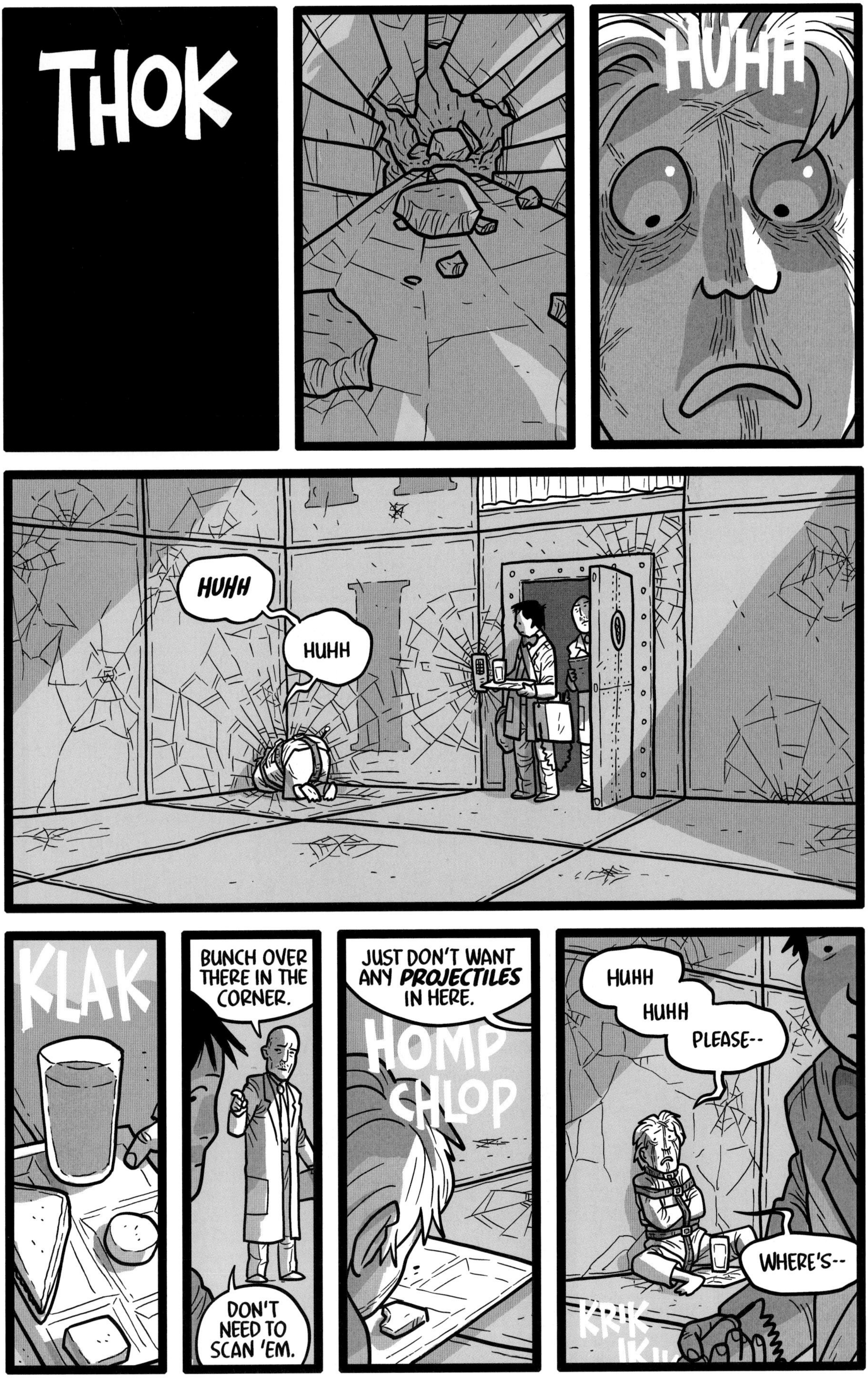
THOK
HUHH
HUHH
HUHH
KLAK
BUNCH OVER THERE IN THE CORNER.
DON'T NEED TO SCAN 'EM.
JUST DON'T WANT ANY PROJECTILES IN HERE.
HOMP
CHLOP
HUHH
HUHH
PLEASE--
WHERE'S--
KRIK

TUMP
TUMP

WHAT IS SHE...?

Oh, GREAT.
BE RIGHT BACK.
Ah...
YOU'RE NOT GOING TO FALL ASLEEP ON ME, ARE YOU?
Haha
Haha
NICOLI

YEAH.
HE HATES YOU.
HE'S BEEN BY A COUPLE TIMES.
SAYING HE'S COMING IN TO KILL YOU.
WE TOLD SECURITY TO KEEP HIM OUT, BUT...
...BEING THE CHIEF OF POLICE WITH A SWAT TEAM AT YOUR BACK AFFORDS YOU CERTAIN PRIVILEGES, I GUESS.
Oh, DON'T WORRY, PHILLIPS WOULD NEVER HAND YOU OVER.
YOU'RE TOO VALUABLE.
BESIDES, I HEAR THAT PEOPLE WHO TRY TO KILL YOU END UP PRETTY DEAD THEMSELVES.
tsk ALL THESE LITTLE POWER STRUGGLES.
ALL RIGHT, LET'S GET--
ARE YOU TALKING TO HIM?
JESUS. YOU CALL YOURSELF A SCIENTIST?
C'MON, LET'S GO.
Oh, ONE SEC, ONE SEC.

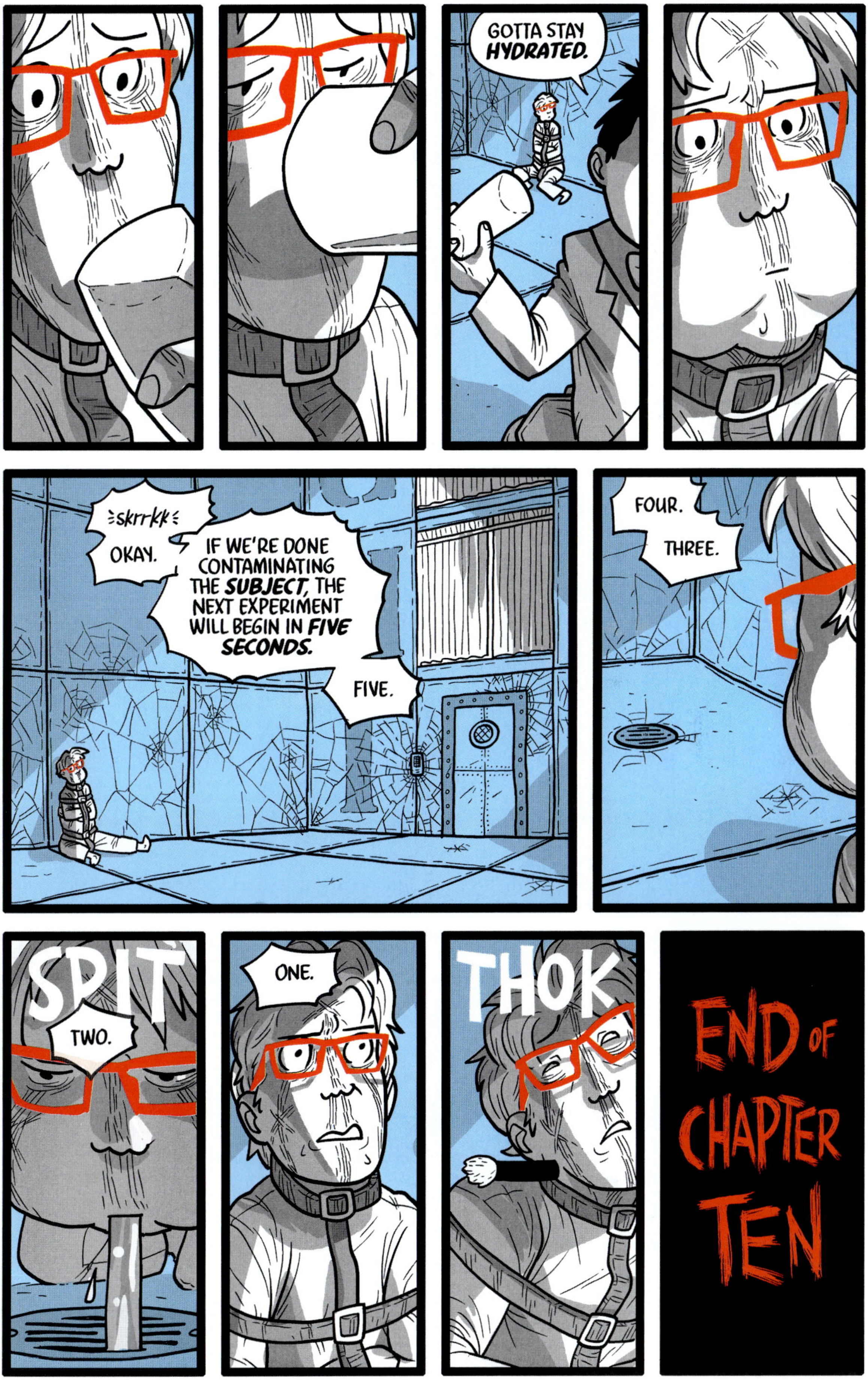
GOTTA STAY *HYDRATED.*
skrrkk
OKAY.
IF WE'RE DONE CONTAMINATING THE *SUBJECT*, THE NEXT EXPERIMENT WILL BEGIN IN *FIVE SECONDS.*
FIVE.
FOUR.
THREE.
SPIT
TWO.
ONE.
THOK
END OF CHAPTER TEN

THOK
HUHH
SPIT
THOK
END OF CHAPTER ELEVEN

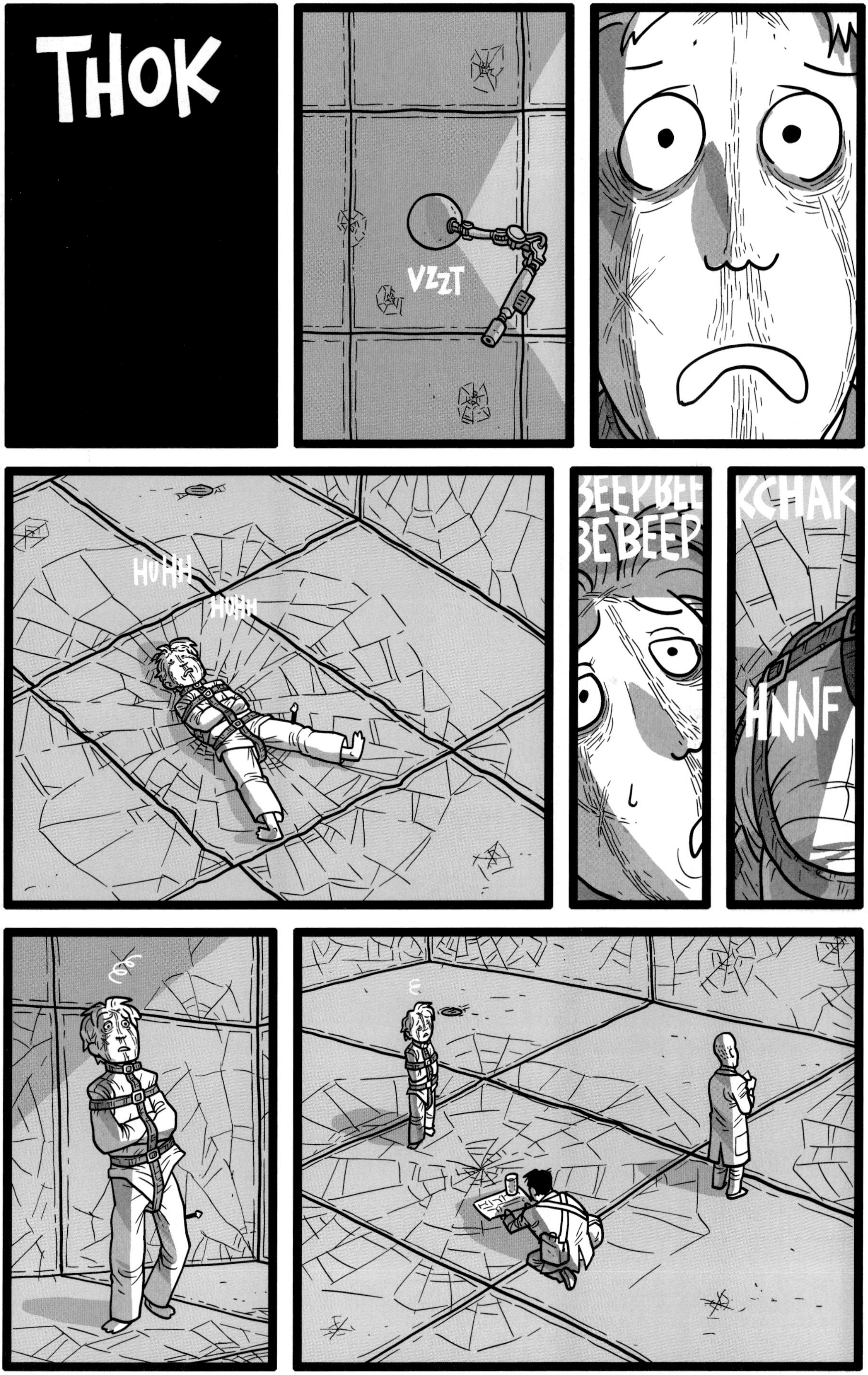
THOK
VZZT
HUHH
HUHH
BEEPBEE
BE BEEP
KCHAK
HNNF

SNRFL
NO, NO.
GIVE ME THOSE. THEY'RE MESSING UP THE READINGS.
I'LL PUT 'EM BACK IN THE LAB.
I CAN'T BELIEVE NOTHING ELSE IN HERE IS SHOWING UP ON THE DAMN SCANS.
H-HEY.
T-TELL ME SOMETHING. WH-WHILE HE'S GONE.
OK, LISTEN, I'M NOT SUPPOSED TO--
PLEASE. Y-YOU'VE SEEN ME, RIGHT?
SEEN YOU?
LIKE, YOU'VE SEEN... WHAT I AM WHEN I'M ASLEEP?
L-LIKE, WHEN I'M A--
YEAH, OKAY. YEAH. I'VE SEEN YOU.
WELL, F-FOR THE LOVE OF GOD...
...WHAT AM I?

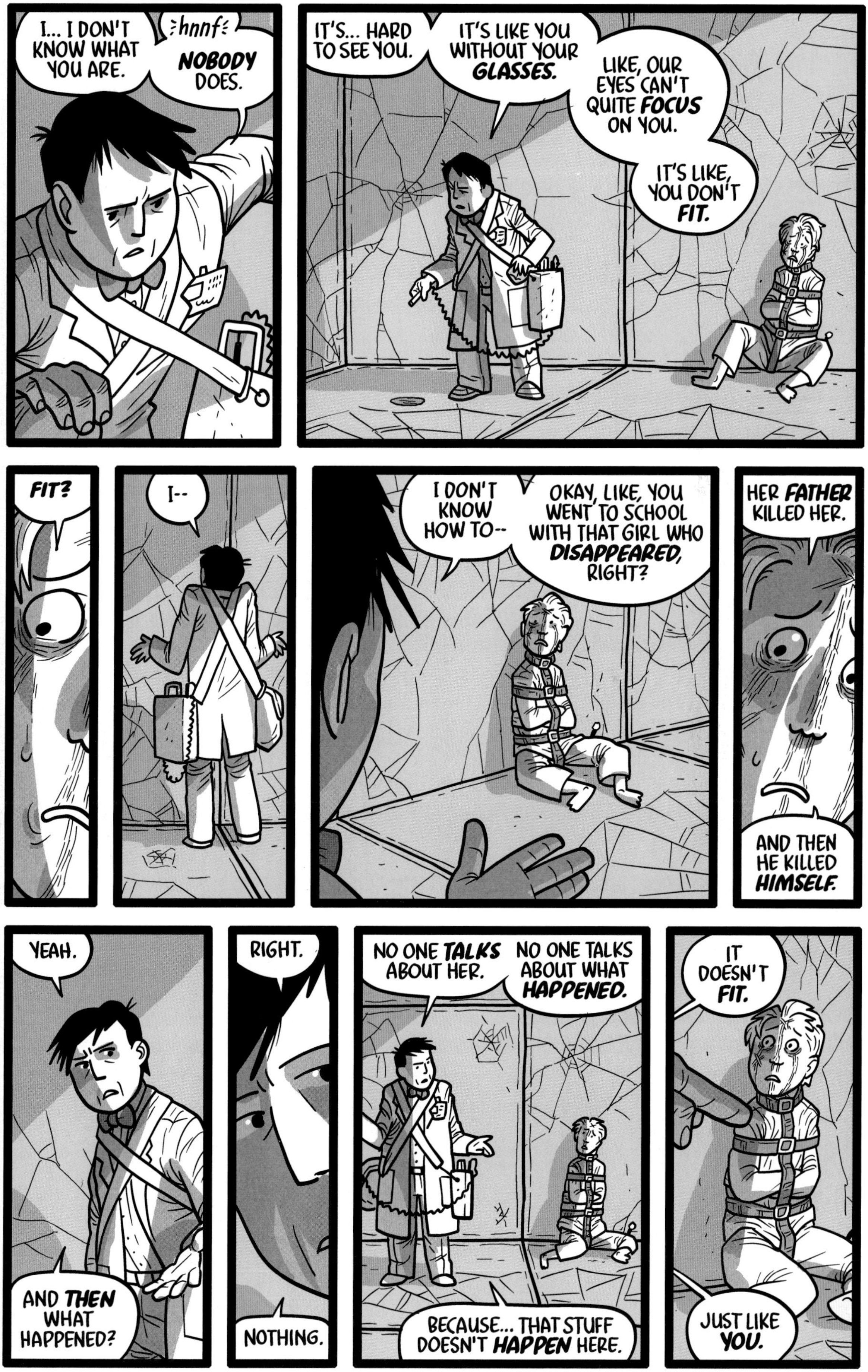
I... I DON'T KNOW WHAT YOU ARE.
hnnf
NOBODY DOES.
IT'S... HARD TO SEE YOU.
IT'S LIKE YOU WITHOUT YOUR GLASSES.
LIKE, OUR EYES CAN'T QUITE FOCUS ON YOU.
IT'S LIKE, YOU DON'T FIT.
FIT?
I--
I DON'T KNOW HOW TO--
OKAY, LIKE, YOU WENT TO SCHOOL WITH THAT GIRL WHO DISAPPEARED, RIGHT?
HER FATHER KILLED HER.
AND THEN HE KILLED HIMSELF.
YEAH.
AND THEN WHAT HAPPENED?
RIGHT.
NOTHING.
NO ONE TALKS ABOUT HER.
NO ONE TALKS ABOUT WHAT HAPPENED.
BECAUSE... THAT STUFF DOESN'T HAPPEN HERE.
IT DOESN'T FIT.
JUST LIKE YOU.

GOD DAMMIT--
I SAID STOP TALKING TO HIM.
WAIT! WAIT!
WHAT DO YOU MEAN JUST LIKE M--
THOK
END OF CHAPTER TWELVE

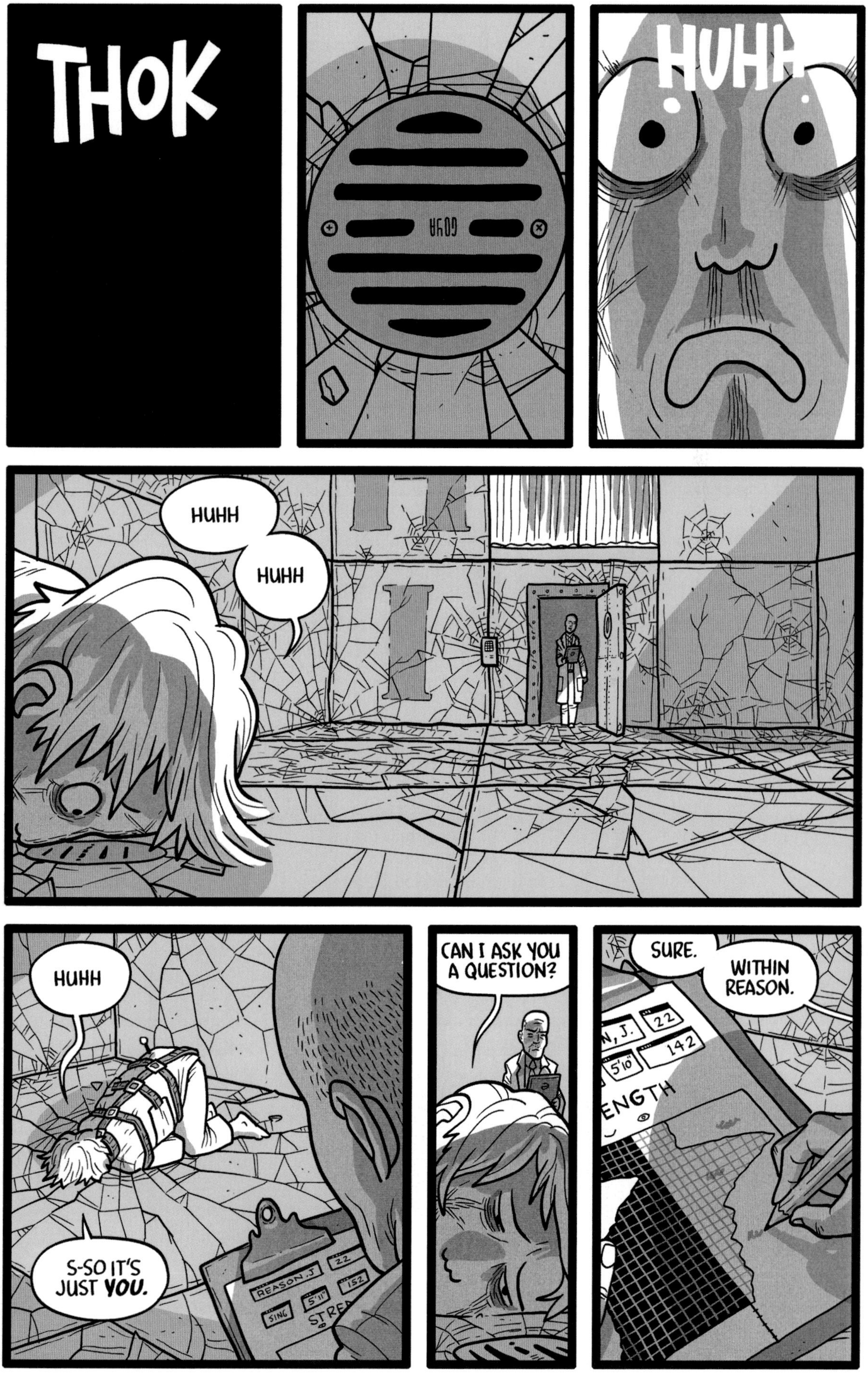
THOK
HUHH
HUHH
HUHH
HUHH
S-SO IT'S JUST **YOU.**
CAN I ASK YOU A QUESTION?
SURE.
WITHIN REASON.

WHAT ARE YOU LEARNING?
WHAT ARE YOU GETTING OUT OF THIS?
YOU'RE NOT CURING ME.
AND YOU'RE NOT KILLING ME.
THOSE ARE THE ONLY OUTCOMES.
JUST... CHOOSE ONE.
Hm.
THAT WAS YOUR PAL TABBY STEVENS' COMPLAINT.
GOT HER PULLED RIGHT OFF THE PROJECT.
SO.
LET ME PUT IT THIS WAY.
YOU'RE GENERATING A LOT OF DATA.
SO YOU'RE USEFUL TO US, CURRENTLY.
YOU ALSO MURDERED A COUPLE DOZEN PEOPLE, INCLUDING THE SON OF THE POLICE CHIEF.
SO MAYBE YOU'LL BE USEFUL TO HIM, LATER.
NOW GET UP.
YEAH.
OKAY.
HNF

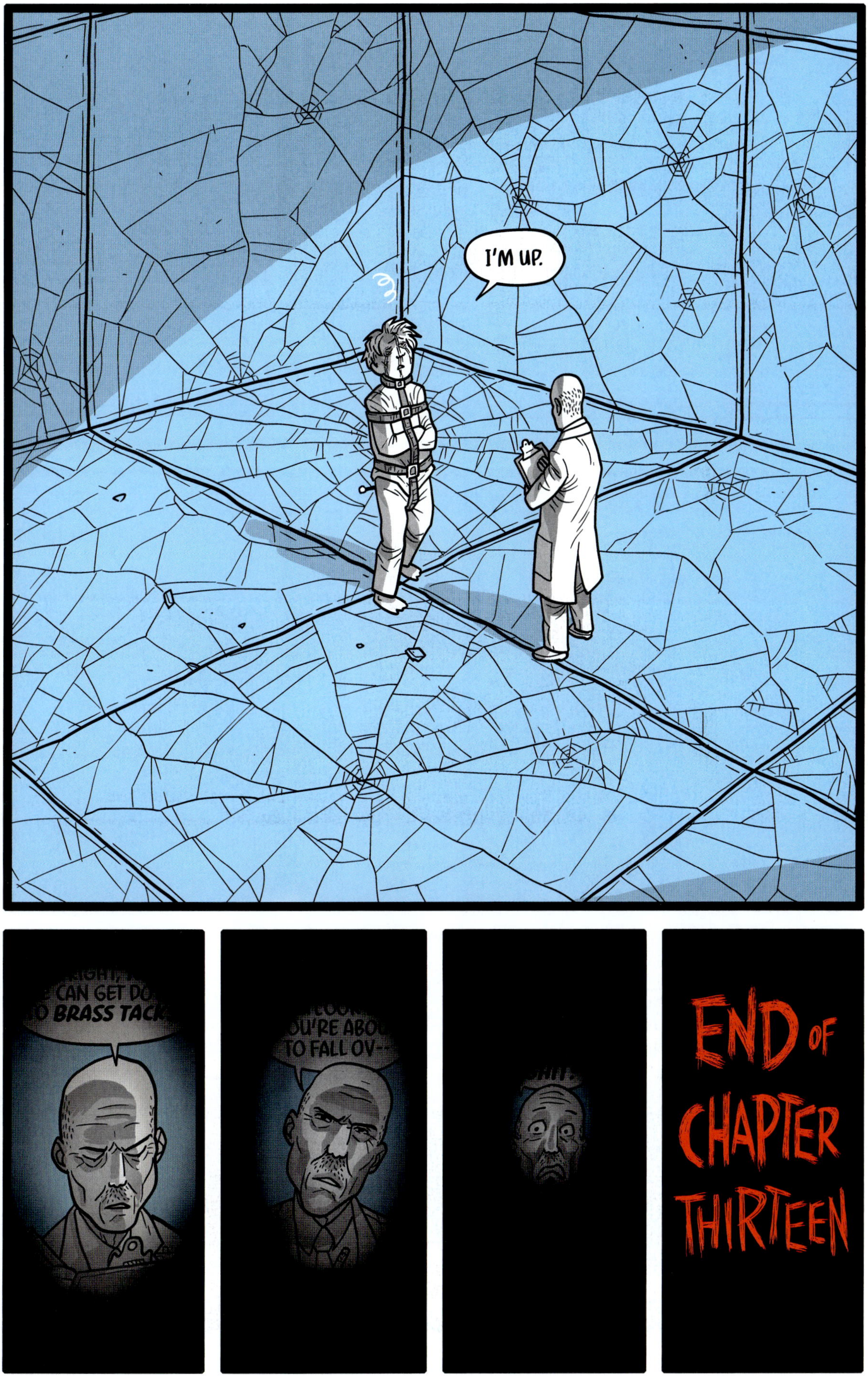
I'M UP.
CAN GET DO
TO BRASS TACK
OU'RE ABO
TO FALL OV--
END OF CHAPTER THIRTEEN

JONATHAN!!

OMIGOD I'M SORRY.
OMIGOD I'M SO SORRY.
TABBY, ARE YOU OKAY?
TABBY?
TABBY, IT'S ME.
WH-WHAT IS IT?
I-IT'S ALL I COULD DO.
I-IN THE TIME I HAD.
IS IT A CURE?
I DON'T KNOW.

I DON'T KNOW IF IT WILL WORK.
sniff
NO ONE ELSE WANTED TO SAVE YOU.
I H-HAD TO TRY.
BUT I-I JUST DON'T KNOW IF--
TABBY.
YOU'RE THE SMARTEST PERSON I KNOW.
STILL.
G-GET SOMEWHERE SAFE, OKA--
END OF CHAPTER FOURTEEN

KIMIRA
MINING™

EIGHT

GOD, PLEASE...
Oh, JESU CHRIST--
WH--
Oh MY GOD Oh
FZZT
WHAT IS--
POP
UP THERE--
NO, GO BACK, G
SLAM
WHERE'M I?
WH-WHERE'S--
--TABBY--

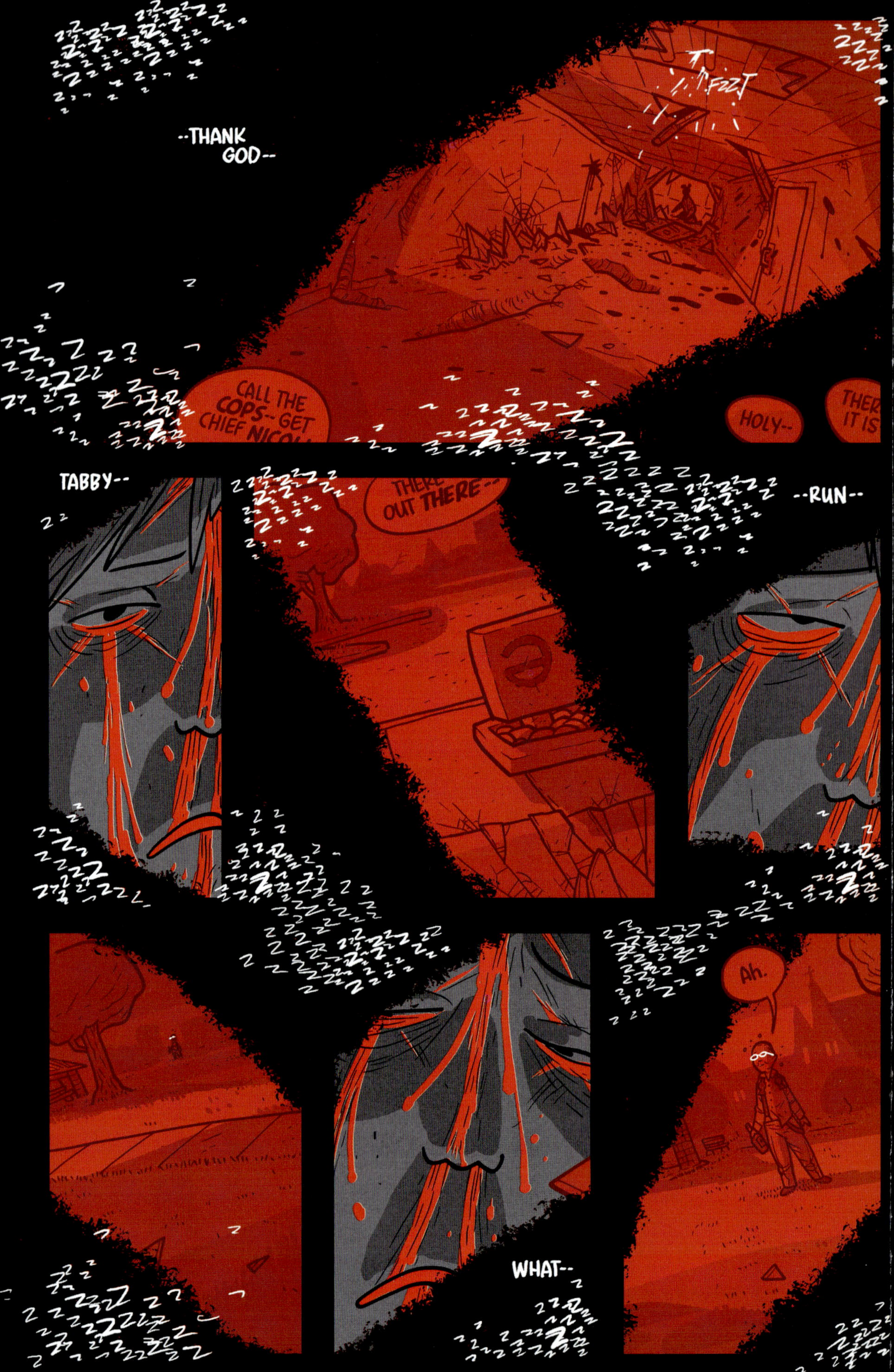
--THANK GOD--
T-FZZT
CALL THE COPS-- GET CHIEF NICO
HOLY--
THER IT IS
TABBY--
THERE OUT THERE--
--RUN--
Ah.
WHAT--

OF COURSE.
OF COURSE.
KRSH
I MIGHT HAVE KNOWN IT WAS YOU.
M-MR. EDISON?
P-PLEASE, SIR, 'M SCARED.
I-I DON' UNNERSTAN' WHAT'S--
I'M READY.

HHK
WHAT--
NO--
NO--
KTAK
OH MY GOD OH MY--
NO, PLEASE--

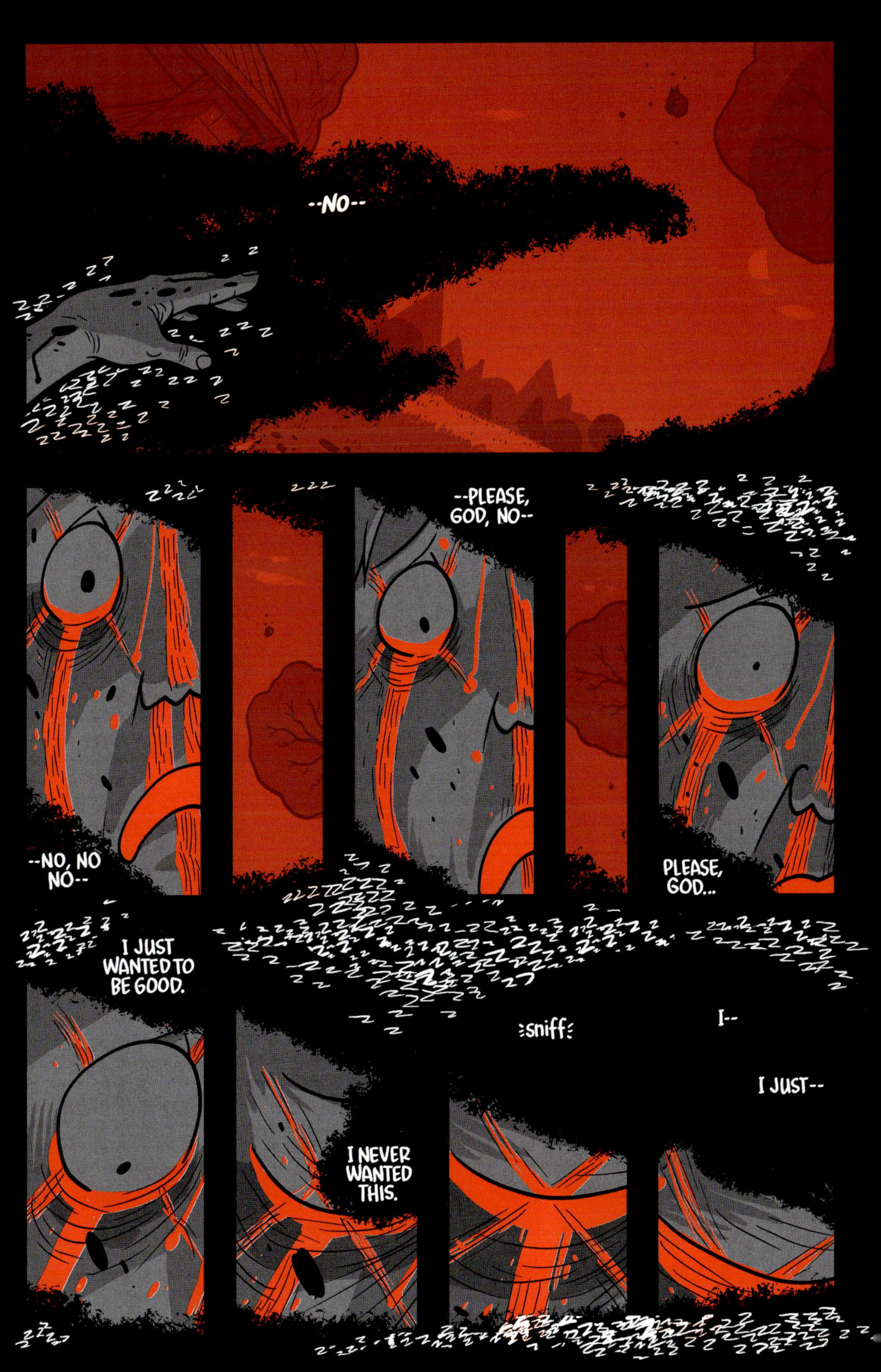
--NO--
--PLEASE, GOD, NO--
--NO, NO NO--
PLEASE, GOD...
I JUST WANTED TO BE GOOD.
sniff
I--
I JUST--
I NEVER WANTED THIS.

THE LAST DAY

NNH--
HUHH
WH--
...CALIE?

THE TEAM'S GOING TO GET A **PIZZA.** SEE YOU THERE?
YEAH. I'LL CATCH UP.
H-HI HONEY. G'JOB OUT THERE.
sigh YEAH, HI, MOM. THANKS.
YOU WERE PLAYING **SO GOOD**, BABY. LIKE A REAL **STAR**, YOU'RE--
SO DID **DAD** COME?
WELL-- MM.
BABY, YOU HAVE TO UNDERSTAND. Y-YOUR DAD GETS REAL **BUSY** SOMETIMES, AND--
YEAH.
BUSY FINDING THE BOTTOM OF A FUCKING **BOTTLE.**

HONEY, WAIT, W-WE JUST--
GOOD GIRL, CALIE! LOOKING GREAT OUT THERE!
Oh, uh, THANKS!
SO THAT WEIRDO CAN COME TO EVERY GAME, AND DAD CAN'T MAKE ONE?
I ASK YOU GUYS FOR ONE S-STUPID THING.
W-WELL, HONEY, LEMME DRIVE YOU BACK TO--
FUCK NO, I'M NOT GETTING IN THAT DEATHTRAP WITH YOU.
GO AND FUCKING DRY OUT. I'LL BE HOME LATER.
TIGERS FOREVER
WAIT--
CALIE, W-WAIT--

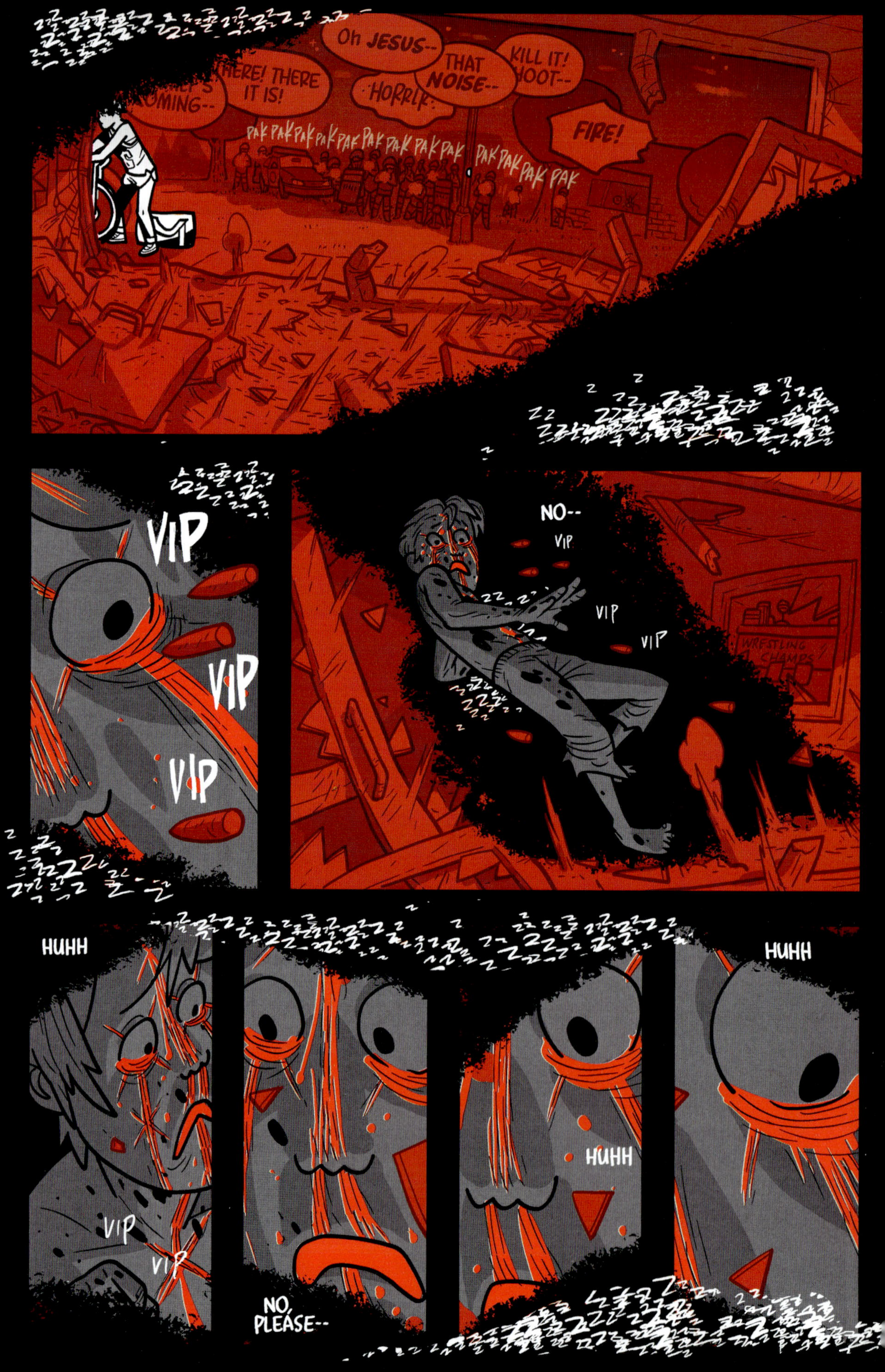
OMING--
HERE! THERE IT IS!
Oh JESUS--
HORRIF
THAT NOISE--
KILL IT! HOOT--
FIRE!
PAK PAK PAK PAK PAK PAK PAK PAK PAK PAK PAK PAK PAK PAK
VIP
VIP
VIP
NO--
VIP
VIP
VIP
HUHH
VIP
VIP
NO, PLEASE--
HUHH
HUHH

HOLY--
WHERE DID IT-
PUNCHED THROUGH TH
I HEAR IT OVER THERE!
--BY THE CHURC
--SO FAST--
--KEEP OOKING--

JERE
JEREMIAH!
OH! Oh, SORRY, PASTOR. I WAS JUST, uh, JUST LOST IN MY OWN THOUGHTS.
I-I'LL BE FINISHED HERE IN JUST A SEC.
MISSING
YOU'RE HERE AWFULLY LATE, AREN'T YOU?
I, uh...
YOU KNOW. IT'S H-HARD TO BE AT HOME.
WITH CALIE GONE...
...I-I FIGURE I BETTER KEEP W-WORKIN' OR I'LL GET A LITTLE STIR-CRAZY.
...MURDERER...
SURE.
CHIEF NICOLI TOLD ME ABOUT YOUR LITTLE TROUBLE THE OTHER WEEK.
YOU WANT TO TALK ABOUT IT?
H-HE TOLD YOU?
O-oh, NO, NO, PASTOR, I DON'T WANNA BOTHER YA.
I JUST NEED TO GET THINGS ORGANIZED HERE, Y'KNOW, KEEP MY M-MIND OFF OF--
sniff
HEY, HEY.
'65-'66
NOT AS A PASTOR.
JUST AS A FRIEND WHO'S GOT A GOOD BOTTLE OF RED OPEN.
RESERVE
O-OPEN?
Oh, GOSH, uh, I DON'T KNOW. I'M TRYIN' TO S-STAY STRAIGHT...
Oh, NOW.
EVEN FOR SPECIAL OCCASIONS?

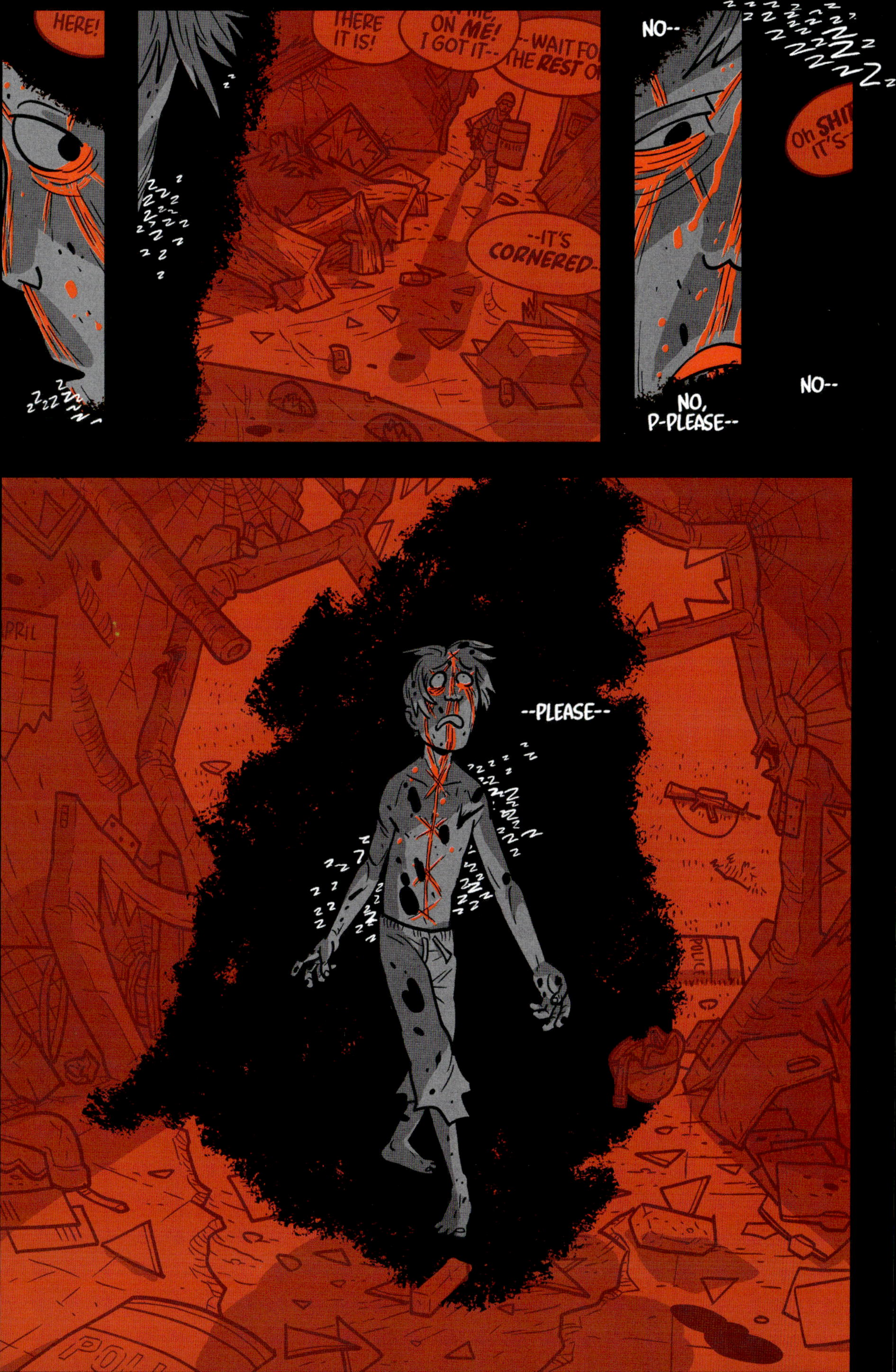
HERE!
THERE IT IS!
ON ME! I GOT IT--
--WAIT FO THE REST O
--IT'S CORNERED--
NO--
Oh SHIT IT'S--
NO, P-PLEASE--
NO--
--PLEASE--

--PLEASE LET THIS END--
TAP TAP
CHIEF NICOLI
OKAY, MR. LAWSON.
JUST A COUPLE FORMS AND WE'LL GET YOU YOUR STUFF BACK.
OKAY.
DO YOU HAVE WORK TODAY?
NO.
THAT'S GOOD. SPEND SOME TIME AT HOME WITH YOUR WIFE. HYDRATE AND ALL THAT.
I-I'M JUST SO SORRY A-ABOUT ALL THIS. I JUST--IT'S BEEN A ROUGH COUPLE DAYS, AN'...
Oh, NOW, I UNDERSTAND. WE ALL DO.
...AN' I GUESS I JUST GOT SO MAD ABOUT H-HOW WE JUST DON'T KNOW ANYTHING.
I KNOW.
BUT MR. LAWSON, I KNOW CALIE WOULD WANT YOU TO TAKE CARE OF YOURSELF.
THAT MEANS GO EASY ON THE DRINKING, OKAY?
I--YEAH. OKAY.
SIGN HERE.
AND HERE. OKAY, YOU'RE ALL SET.
HOLD ON. ONE MORE, JEREMIAH.
NOTHING BIG.
JUST GOT TO CROSS OUR T'S AND DOT OUR I'S, Y'KNOW.

GREAT.
LEAVE IT TO US.
JUST STAY ON THE WAGON, hm? THAT'S WHAT SHE'D WANT.
SURE, SURE...
Y'KNOW.
SAVE IT FOR SPECIAL OCCASIONS.
NNH
HUHH
KIMIRA

NNFF
sniff
"REAL BUSY"
SHIT!
OWW
OWW, GOD...
NNFF
GOD DAMN IT.
S-STUPID...
HELLO THERE! RUN INTO A PROBLEM?

Oh!
uh...
Hm, LOOKS LIKE A NASTY SCRAPE THERE.
GOTTA GET THAT TAKEN CARE OF.
Oh, uh, NO, THAT'S OKAY, MR. EDISON. I CAN MANAGE--
Oh, HO HO, NOT WITH THAT BIKE YOU WON'T.
MY SHOP'S JUST AROUND THE CORNER.
NO TROUBLE AT ALL.
THERE!
FINALLY--
--LOOKS BIGGER--
--CHIEF WAS RIGHT--
--HOLD YOUR FIRE--
--HOLY--

STOP RIGHT THERE...
...JONATHAN.
POLICE

...CHIEF NICOLI?
I KNOW IT'S YOU IN THERE.
YOU THAT'S DESTROYED THIS TOWN.
YOU THAT KILLED MY SON.
PLEASE, CHIEF...

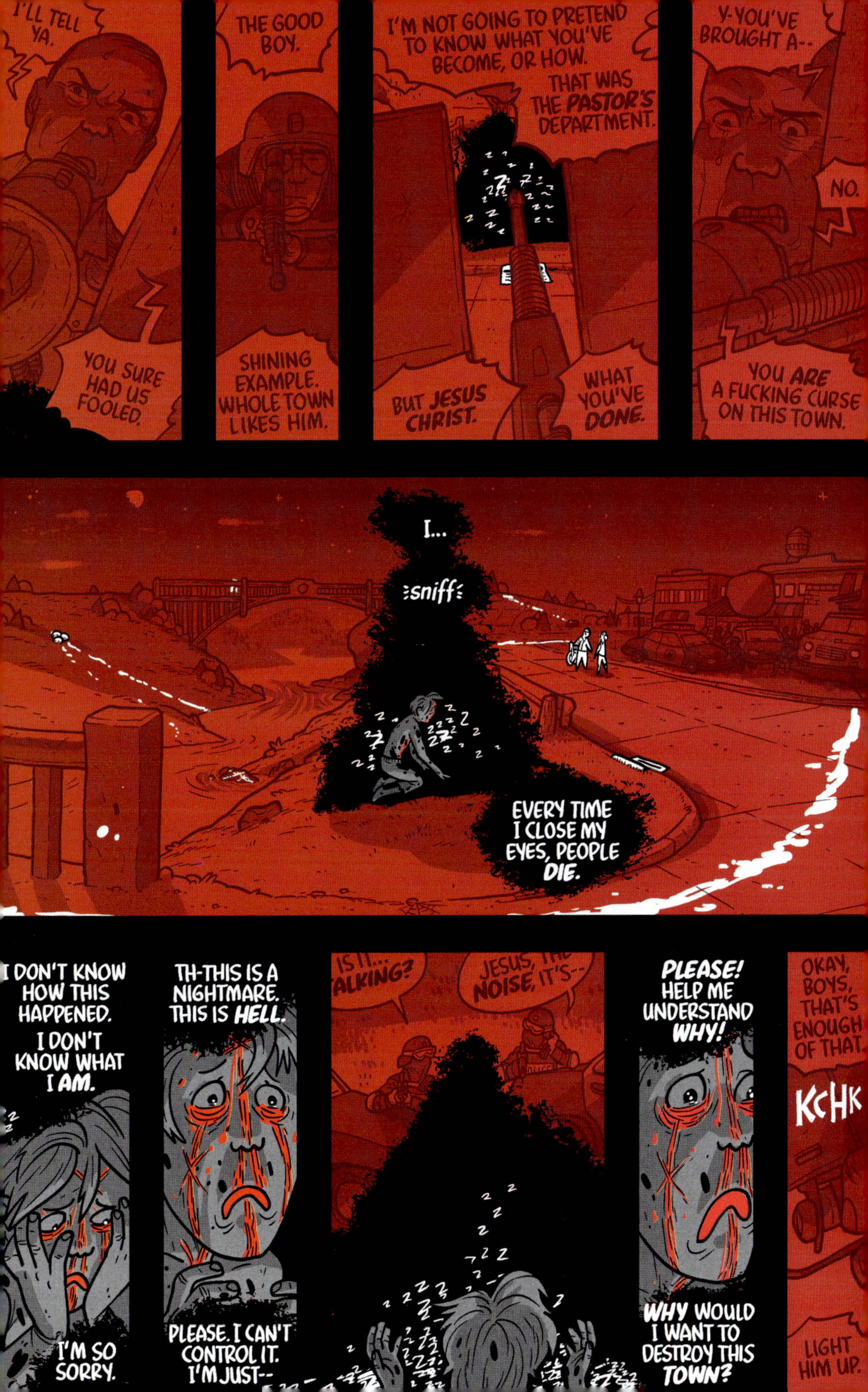
I'LL TELL YA.
YOU SURE HAD US FOOLED.
THE GOOD BOY.
SHINING EXAMPLE. WHOLE TOWN LIKES HIM.
I'M NOT GOING TO PRETEND TO KNOW WHAT YOU'VE BECOME, OR HOW.
THAT WAS THE PASTOR'S DEPARTMENT.
BUT JESUS CHRIST.
WHAT YOU'VE DONE.
Y-YOU'VE BROUGHT A--
NO.
YOU ARE A FUCKING CURSE ON THIS TOWN.
I...
sniff
EVERY TIME I CLOSE MY EYES, PEOPLE DIE.
I DON'T KNOW HOW THIS HAPPENED.
I DON'T KNOW WHAT I AM.
I'M SO SORRY.
TH-THIS IS A NIGHTMARE. THIS IS HELL.
PLEASE. I CAN'T CONTROL IT. I'M JUST--
PLEASE! HELP ME UNDERSTAND WHY!
WHY WOULD I WANT TO DESTROY THIS TOWN?
OKAY, BOYS, THAT'S ENOUGH OF THAT.
KCHK
LIGHT HIM UP.

PAK PAK PAK PAK PAK PAK PAK PAK PAK PAK
CHD CHD CHD
PAK PAK PAK PAK PAK
VIP
VIP
VIP
VIP
VIP
VIP
VIP
VIP
HUHH
BIKE OKAY, MR. EDISON?
HAHA! ALL GOOD, MY DEAR.
UH, YEAH, I GUESS SO.
HUHH
YOU'RE BREATHING KIND OF
I-IT'S BEEN SOME TIME SINC YOU'VE BEE

PROBABLY SINCE MY DAD GOT NEW GLASSES.
Oh YES, I REMEMBER VERY WELL, CALIE.
YOU... MADE QUITE AN IMPRESSION.
HA HA, I GUES-- OWW!
WHAT-- STOP!!
A BLOOD-BATH--
BE READY IF HE--
--MY GOD--
--SMASHED THROUGH THE
NO, MIST--
HHK
KK
GGK

HKK
NO
Oh GOD NO
NO, NO, NO

Z Z Z Z Z Z Z Z Z Z
CAR
SLAM
VRRRN
HUHH

Oh GOD
NNF
Oh GOD, WHERE AM I?
EHNF
Oh NO NO NO.
MISTER EDISON, HE--
Oh GOD P-PLEASE HELP ME.
FIRE!!
GOD, PLEASE D-DON'T LET ME DIE LIKE THIS.
THERE!
--CIRCLE AROUND--
PLEASE, GOD--
THERE! HERE HE IS!!
--HEADED FOR THE BRIDGE--
PLEASE--
PAK PAK
PAK PAK
PAK PAK PAK PAK
--STAY WITH HIM--
POUR IT ON--
GET PAST HIM! GET--
VIP
VIP
VIP
PLEASE--
--THINK HE'S HURT--
MOVE! MOVE!!
PAK
PAK PAK PAK
VIP
VIP
VIP

--MOVE IN--
MOVE--
HGK--
GHLK
HEY CHIEF...
THAT'S JEREMIAH LAWSON'S CAR.
HM. LOOKS PRETTY BAD.
LET ME CHECK IT OUT.
GET--
HGK
DEAD?
YEP.
PLAP

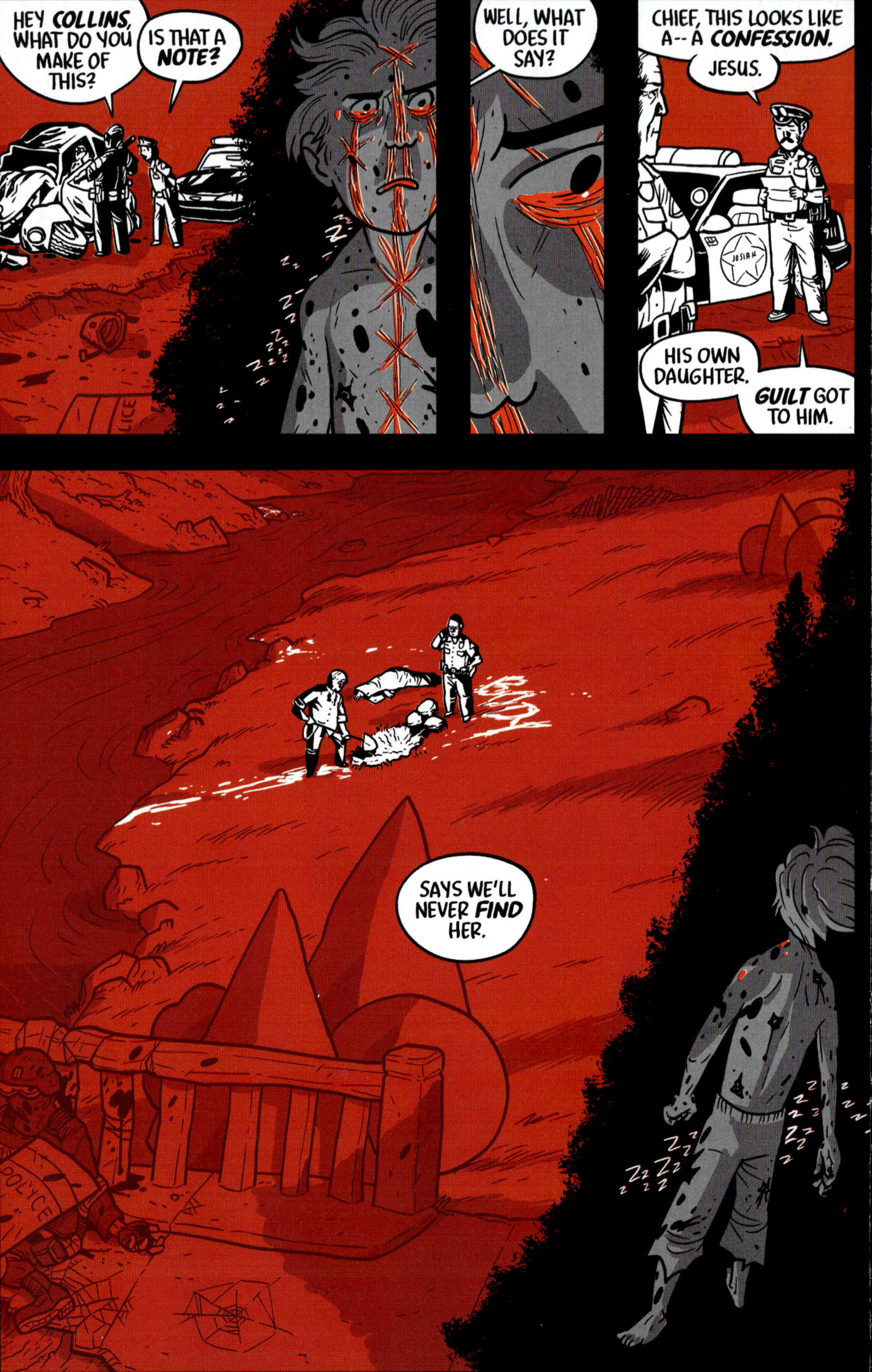
HEY COLLINS, WHAT DO YOU MAKE OF THIS?
IS THAT A NOTE?
WELL, WHAT DOES IT SAY?
CHIEF, THIS LOOKS LIKE A-- A CONFESSION.
JESUS.
HIS OWN DAUGHTER.
GUILT GOT TO HIM.
SAYS WE'LL NEVER FIND HER.

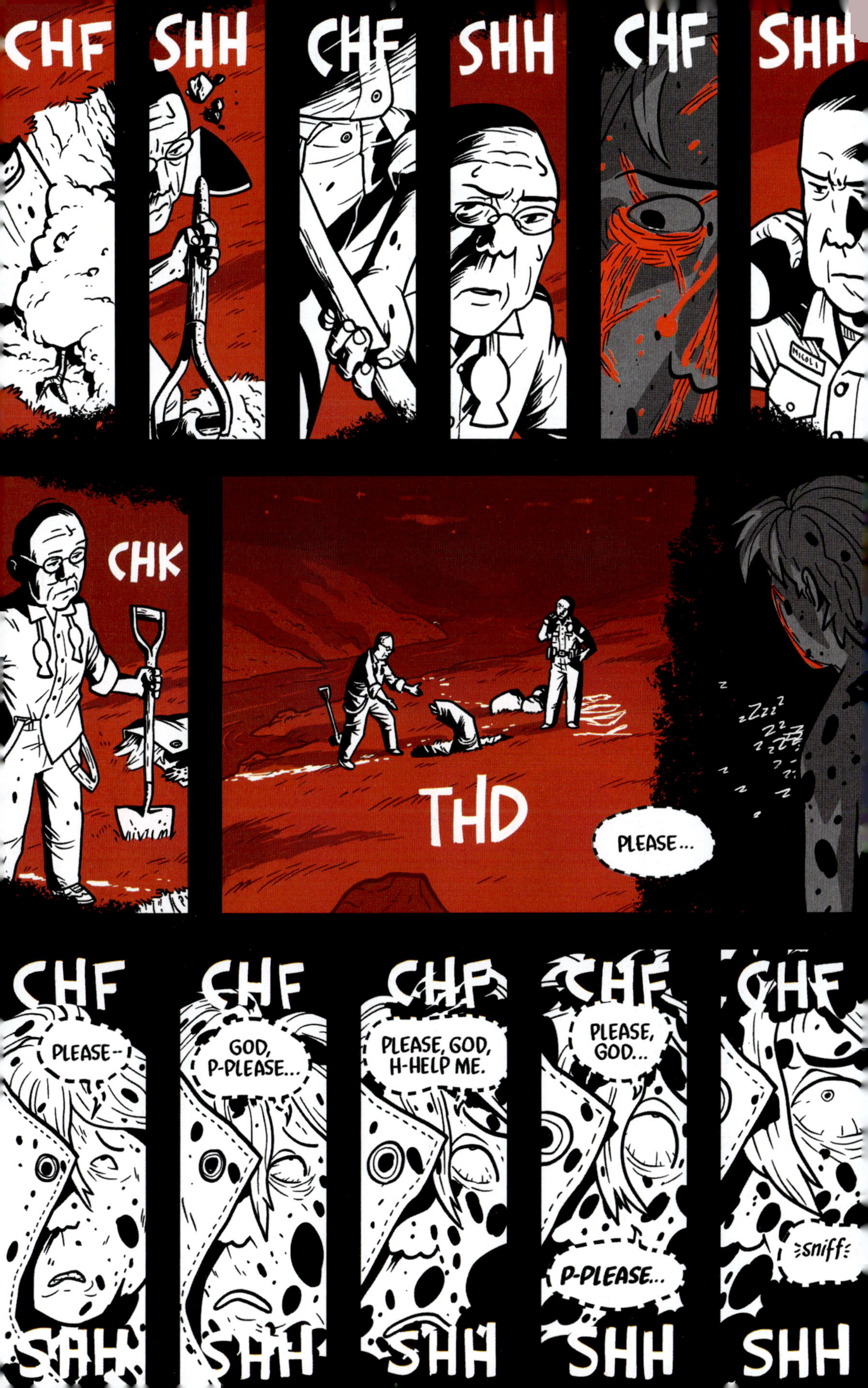
CHF
SHH
CHF
SHH
CHF
SHH
NICOLI
CHK
THD
PLEASE...
CHF
PLEASE--
SHH
CHF
GOD, P-PLEASE...
SHH
CHF
PLEASE, GOD, H-HELP ME.
SHH
CHF
PLEASE, GOD...
P-PLEASE...
SHH
CHF
sniff
SHH

...ANYONE.
SKREEEEE

KTUNK
YOU EVIL PIECE OF SHIT.
ALL THESE MEN. YOU--*
JESUS...
YOU...
YOU EVIL PIECE OF SHIT.
SLAM
VRNNN
YOU EVIL PIECE OF--

KRASH
KISH
TINKLE
UNK
KKLU
HKK
KKH
KTUMP

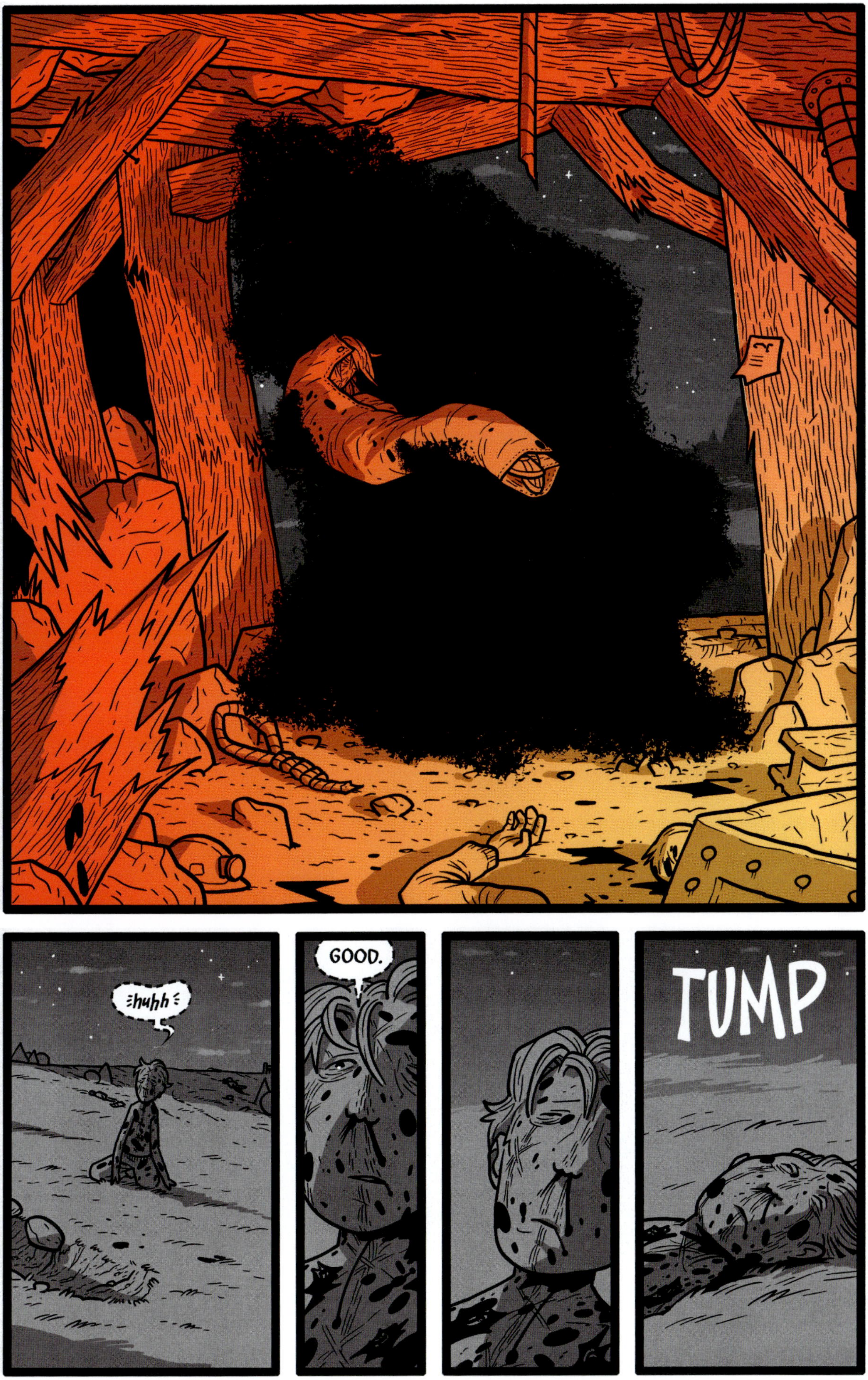
huhh
GOOD.
TUMP

GOOD.

ORIGINAL PITCH DOCUMENT

The idea for *Sleep* originated many years ago in college as a couple different ideas that I ended up combining. I liked 1. the idea of an evil guardian angel (I had started writing it as a play, strangely enough) and 2. the idea of telling a werewolf story (a favorite horror premise of mine) from a strictly limited – that is to say, human – point of view.

In any case, the basic premise and structure of *Sleep* had been kicking around in my head for at least 20 years as I worked on other projects, until I decided to write this proposal, which I now present here as, if nothing else, a pitch that got picked up.

PREMISE

The premise is simple: a Jekyll/Hyde situation in which a young man named Jonathan Reason turns into some kind of horrifying creature when he sleeps. But the hook of SLEEP is how it's told: putting the reader in his shoes, each issue of the comic takes place from the moment he wakes up until the moment he falls asleep. The intention is to omit the action and the chaos and intensify the mystery, horror, and sense of gruesome discovery. Every morning he wakes to realize he has terrorized the town he's in, destroyed everything in his path, and left piles of bodies in his wake, and he is on the run to determine how to stop it.

CHARACTERS

JONATHAN

A young man in his 20s, having recently graduated from the local Christian college, now lives a sheltered life in the small town where he grew up. His parents have died. He tries to be a true-blue Christian, really walking the walk, and so far his life hasn't been complicated enough to test him on it. Works in a coffee shop as he sorts out what he wants his life to be. He continually insists that he wants to "do good" and tends to reject career paths that he perceives to be morally compromising (using Tabitha's pharmaceutical job as an example).

TABITHA

A young woman that Jonathan knows from church. They are friends, and she is another true-blue believer. Tabitha, a science geek, quickly found work for a pharmaceutical company out of college, which brought her to this little town. Ambitious, driven, hardworking, energetic, and thorough, she is constantly eager to prove herself but can be a touch self-centered.

HIPP

A longtime friend of Jonathan's, who has begun recently to play the guitar for the church's band. He was chasing his dreams elsewhere -- in a large American midwestern city -- until abruptly coming back to town to live with his parents. Mostly tight-lipped about the details of his "rock star days," as he calls them, he has instead embraced a hardline version of Christianity that is about "a return to decency and a rejection of degeneracy."

Sleep is in the format that I typically write my proposals, which breaks down what I imagine publishers want to know, and in the order they want to know it. I like to start with a clearly defined premise. This is going to largely make or break the proposal, especially if you are not well known, so it behooves you to spend a fair bit of time crafting it. I try to describe the premise both "in-universe" (i.e. the elements that the characters are aware of, the problems that have to be solved, etc.) and from a reader's point of view (i.e. it's a mystery, it's a serialized story, the storytelling is a little idiosyncratic, etc.).

I also like putting the characters front and center. Plot is great and all, but people love characters and won't be interested if the characters aren't appealing. There is a fair bit here in the descriptions that the story doesn't really get into in much detail, but it's nice to have a sense for what a character is like even beyond their "type."

STRUCTURE

The eight chapters, as mentioned, are told from the moment Jonathan wakes up until the moment he goes to sleep, which roughly -- but not exactly -- break down by day: Sunday to Sunday. Each of the various instances of falling asleep and waking up chart the process of his realization, his hope that it's temporary, his strategy to minimize the damage, his denial, his anger, his bargaining, his depression, and finally, his acceptance and the grim use of this "gift."

The issues detail his moment-by-moment movement:

SUNDAY. Wakes up, terrible taste in mouth. While walking to the bathroom, kneels down to put cat food in the bowl, then looks up to see that the front door to his house is wide open. Before he can even fully think about it, the phone rings. It's a friend of his, Tabitha. She's anxious, wondering where he is; she thought he'd meet her at church. He looks at the clock, sees he's late. He says he's got to find his cat, but it'll probably be fine. She's much more intense and says no, that he should get the cat back inside asap-- did he hear about what happened last night? She gives him a description of a gruesome series of crimes and sightings of …something. As she's talking, he sees an ambulance wail by outside. He moves toward the front door and as his view of the front of his house widens, he sees deep gouges in the ground, shattered fences, an overturned car, debris everywhere. A reverse shot shows his house as he looks out the front door with an enormous blood splatter across it. The rest of the issue is him meeting up with friends at church and discussing what is going on. We get introduced to his circle of acquaintances, including Tabitha and Hipp, a friend from childhood who's recently returned to town and now plays for the church band. Discussions range between practical matters of locking doors, trivial matters like returning something someone borrowed or what the pastor said, practical matters like almost getting eviscerated, etc. The rest of the day is composed of running errands, helping stores sweep up glass, and generally giving readers the layout of the town. He still can't find his cat. In bed that night, he has a moment to think. All the little clues here and there, including small wounds on his body, lead him to suspect, as he reaches over in his bed and finds his missing cat's collar, that he might actually be responsible.

MONDAY. Jonathan wakes up in the bushes near his home. Terrified. Hides from passersby, then hears the clock tower strike 9 and realizes he's late for work. He rushes home and gets dressed. His day at work has him in a fog as he tries to figure out what's going on. He meets Hipp for lunch and tries to keep up with the usual bro-talk, some of which is about the farmhouse out in the sticks that was obliterated, some of which is how Hipp suspects

Again, I like to give a little bit of context before I jump into the story. If you've spent some time working up the plot of your story, it can be pretty tempting to really get into the weeds with it, so in addition to trying not to do that, I also like to give a rough overview so that the reader/editor/publisher has a sense for what the basic shape of this story is.

that Tabitha is in love with Jonathan. The tinge of jealousy is lost on Jonathan; he's too distracted. As he walks back to work, he starts looking at some of the bars that stores are putting in their windows and thinks about how he might need to think about a place that he can sleep that can hold him in. The rest of the day progresses with him worrying about it but not quite knowing if he's right. He eats dinner in his house/apartment, but looks around and realizes he's afraid to go to sleep. He goes out for a walk, loaded with anxiety. He's tired, he sits down. A cop comes and harasses him, moving him along. Jonathan loses his temper and screams at the cop. There's a tense moment when Jonathan knows he should deescalate, but he has a thought and punches the cop. He's arrested, booked, and thrown in a jail cell. There's another person in his cell, who's aggressive and unpleasant, but Jonathan still thinks he would be collateral damage. He flails around and acts deranged until the cellmate requests to leave. He's exhausted, but as the cell doors close, it's now safe, he can finally go to sleep.

TUESDAY. He wakes up in his own bed. It takes a second for it to dawn on him what that means. It's early, so he ventures outside (splintered door to apartment), and discovers a swath of destruction that leads back to a police station that's an absolute slaughterhouse. He takes a moment to see that even the cellmate has been killed.

This is the moment he realizes that solving this is going to take more than little precautions.

The rest of the issues involve Jonathan -- with increasing desperation -- attempting to undo the problems he's caused and prevent further atrocities, including by hitchhiking hundreds of miles away (wakes up in town again, a scorched path of burning wreckage behind him), by locking himself in a mine (wakes up above ground, cooling lava all around), and even jumping off a bridge to commit suicide (wakes up 30 miles downriver, in a pile of corpses), all while guiltily hiding his involvement from people in the town. After rapidly running out of logical ideas, Jonathan enlists Tabitha's help. With her intelligence and scientific skillset and Jonathan's desperation, there are a number of places to try out intuitive, intelligent solutions and give them horrendous consequences.

Interwoven with all this is the drama of his friend group, one aspect of which is Hipp becoming both obsessed with Tabitha and with the apocalyptic nature of the creature and its rampages. Having seen what he considered to be divine retribution reflected in the violence that's been done to the town, he becomes a touch unhinged and starts intensely pursuing Tabitha. His language keeps circling the ideas that the old ways are dead and that

After the opening couple chapters, which are pretty cleanly defined, I felt like I could back off of the specifics and summarize the rest of the story, up until the last scene. With some splashy images, I felt like I could basically say that the story played out according to genre rules and here are some vibes. Unless someone is demanding that you provide them with a full script, I feel like a little looseness is allowable here.

the spoils will go to the strong, etc. When -- while hiding away in a makeshift bomb shelter overnight -- Hipp's attempted seduction of Tabitha goes awry, and he hits her, then runs out into the night, heedless of the creature. That is the morning that Jonathan wakes up in a space, a place with some quality -- scientific, or religious, or a combination of the two, that he and Tabitha figured out -- that works: It is filled with debris, splintered wood and torn metal, but it kept him inside all night. He is weakly celebrating until he hears a faint ringing. He searches around, and finds an emergency telephone in the rubble, and it is her on the other end, telling him what has happened.

The climax in the final issue is the confrontation between Jonathan and Hipp, in which he finally gives up his most strongly held belief -- that of trying to do no harm. Leaving the one safe place he's found, Jonathan searches out this former friend of his, and time seems to slow. Where most 22 page issues span 16+ hours in Jonathan's life, this one is only about 30 minutes. His journey has taken him from self preservation and not making waves to becoming a perverse instrument of justice. He finds Hipp, who in his fury and guilt makes bold pronouncements about how the world should be and how the weak should bow to the strong. Jonathan, furious, exhausted, depleted, keeps advancing but makes no move to defend himself. Hipp becomes wild with rage, screaming that they should never have pushed him. Jonathan has made his decision, and so the last thing he sees as he slowly advances, arms at his sides, is Hipp swinging a golf club at his head, then black (and -- we assume -- an extremely messy murder).

The stories are going to be light on dialogue and heavy on meaningful visual detail, if the reader knows where to look. Specific damage to certain places, brand names, props established in one place that show up in another, a secret lab, evidence of a covered-up mining accident from long ago, subtleties in clothing choices and changes, recurring character names of people we never see, etc. This is a book with chapters meant to be reread and combed for clues, all to enrich what is -- on the surface -- a pretty straightforward thriller.

VISUAL STYLE

I intend to make the series with a more limited palette, possibly to the point of being only grayscale, with the intention of using that to draw more attention to the lighting and the foreboding atmosphere, as well as to mute the gore and focus more on the existential horror of Jonathan's situation.

Depending on the price points for various printing styles, it might make sense to have the ability to pop in a single color, as a baked-in lore signal. For instance, red objects are those directly related to a long-ago inciting incident that is only alluded to in the course of the characters' emotional arcs.

Again, taking a moment outside of the narrative to address some practical matters of printing, storytelling style, and the reader experience shows that this series is ready to pivot around certain realities as they present themselves.

The print department and I investigated the savings in having only 2 colors for the series. As it happens, having black and a specially mixed red ink would have been twice as expensive as a regular 4-color book, so *Sleep* ended up being a color comic that merely had a disciplined approach to its color channels. That certainly was nice when adding a tiny bit of color on one page didn't trigger a budget discussion.

SETTING+LORE

SETTING: The story is a bit of a period piece, based in the '90s: modern enough to seem relevant, but just before the surveillance state was in full swing, in order to head off questions about cameras that would now be everywhere. The setting will be in a small midwestern town, small enough for the story to, in the course of telling a narrative, give the reader a more or less complete sense for its layout.

LORE: It's never explicitly stated, but the implication is that the creature is some kind of minor devil, which doesn't matter except in that the intensity of its rampages are inversely related to how good Jonathan is trying to be in his waking hours. The better he's trying to be, the worse the rampages, and vice versa.

LOGIC: Each of the between-issue rampages will be planned out in detail, creating a completely separate, parallel story that we see bits and pieces of in the visual details of the wreckage. The creature has its own motivations and goals, none of which are of any importance to the story of Jonathan trying to find the most ethical way out of the predicament he's in, but may influence further stories. They also form a crucial logical backbone to the story which might otherwise read as pure allegory. The goal will be to make sure that it is possible, with careful attention to detail, to piece together the timeline of the creature's rampages, broadly discern its motivations, and connect a few dots here and there, without having it affect the main narrative.

GOING FORWARD

SECOND SEASON: If the stories were to continue, a second season would look like this: Since good intentions (i.e. counter to the desires of the creature) result in it getting stronger/more evil in the sleep phase, the reverse is also true. Jonathan's "evil" desire to kill this former friend resulted in a creature that is weaker, and hence, when he wakes up for the start of this new season, he is in a lab, where he has been captured by a mysterious corporation (that will be alluded to many times in the first series). Him being isolated and experimented on gives this series a similar feeling of a lack of information and focus on the minute-to-minute details of his life (e.g. looking for clues, finding a way to escape, gaming the mechanics of his sleep system, etc.). Similarly to the first season, it would be 8 issues, over roughly a week.

THIRD SEASON: A third season, in which he has escaped and tries to both find his way back to Tabitha and work to resolve the central goals of -- and thereby either free or destroy -- the creature, is also possible.

Eagle-eyed readers will notice that much of the information on this page is either not touched on much, reorganized, or ignored entirely in the final product. That can happen! I felt like the later bits of the story could be compressed somewhat as we went hurtling toward the finish. Typically, if these changes are relegated to less-creative elements (length of story, for example) it's less of a problem than, say, changing the actual events of the plot.

This section is intentionally loose and has the feeling of spitballing rather than locking anything down. Again, having the sense of being able to adjust certain aspects of the project around the realities of the comic book market can be a plus when pitching to budget-minded publishers.

PUBLICATION STRATEGY

SERIALIZATION: The main (gimmicky) hook for the book is the disconnect between the end of an issue and the beginning of the next. All the blood and gore and violence that would be in a more over-the-top horror story takes place in the unseen gap, giving the moment before reading the first page of the next issue a little whir of excitement. In that way, the sort-of-necessary-evil of serialization can instead work in SLEEP's favor: giving a moment for people to think about some of the details of the previous issue and speculate as to what could be happening. I think at long last this might be the project of mine that is actually perfectly suited to the monthly 22-page comic format.

COVERS: In addition to keeping readers on tenterhooks with the cliffhangers and implications for what happens in between, one approach to getting readers to opt in every month could be: the covers form a massive panorama linking all 8 of the wraparound images together, full of Easter eggs that only make sense once the reader has read the whole story. Even reproducing these images in an eventual trade paperback won't quite have the same effect; you gotta track down those issues!

FREQUENCY: Now, with a single creator, a monthly book is a big ask even for a limited series, but I suspect that with implicit cliffhangers at the end of every issue, it's crucial. And if it's necessary to bank several issues in order to keep on schedule anyway, it might be worthwhile to consider releasing one every 3 weeks or even 2 weeks, just to relentlessly keep it on people's minds.

POSSIBLE OTHER FORMATS: Alternatively, if there were a prominent way to release it digitally, the book might be suited to digital chapters of smaller pages with a longer page count, and then only release the story physically once it's entirely done in a manga-sized TPB. Being able to quickly check back on an easily accessible previous chapter could smooth the buy-in for readers, and furthermore, the dialogue-light storytelling and periodic gore reveals could be something that -- if put in front of people's eyes on social media -- could serve very well as its own marketing.

Another page of scattered thoughts. As I had a basic template ready to go (32-page magazines on a more or less monthly schedule), I thought it might be worth it to toss out a couple other ideas in case that was something that appealed.

It's worth mentioning that there are several things not included in this proposal that a younger person might need, in order to be considered:

Sequential pages. I have been drawing comics for over 30 years, so I can reasonably assume that a publisher or editor knows that I can do the job. That being said, if I was taking this to a publishing house that was outside the comics/graphic novel world, I would probably knock out a couple pages just to prove it.

Script. Sometimes people want to see it, again, if they are not familiar with your work and either want to see if your style is what they're looking for, or assuage their fears that you won't be able to finish writing it.

MARKETING

"Sleep" as a title has bad SEO, and you'd think I would have learned my lesson with "Heck". My name, on the other hand, is pretty unique so that always helps. That said, I also like "The Sleep of Reason", as in: the kid's last name is Reason, and it calls back to that Goya print "The Sleep of Reason Produces Monsters", which could also be used as a visual motif throughout. Either way you'll probably have to pair it with my name to get the correct hits, but those are the options.

With a naturalistic art style and no visuals of the horrendous creature, the book really ought to be marketed to be of a type with the recent crop of lower-budget, tightly-plotted horror films that have come out in the last few years. Less focus on spectacle and more on pacing, character, and grim visceral thrills. Readers ought to go in with the sense of methodically but nervously trying to figure out what is going on, rather than waiting for a big visual setpiece.

I believe this series, with its tight plot, gruesome reveals, hidden lore, and relatable struggles, can find a sizable audience in world of both horror and high-concept serialized comics.

Thank you for reading.
Pleasant dreams!

Zander Cannon
Minneapolis, 2023

Pitches are really interesting to me, since they are frequently fairly different than the project they spawn. Usually, and most obviously, it's character designs, but mine always diverge from the number of issues, how they're organized, and the tone they get across. I always feel like there's a moment of supreme clarity when you actually have to make a cover, write solicitation copy, and fit your story into 22-27 pages. Suddenly all the loose ideas that you've been considering become either very clearly bad or very clearly good and you create a project that is similar, but not the same, as the one you've been idly thinking about for 30 years.

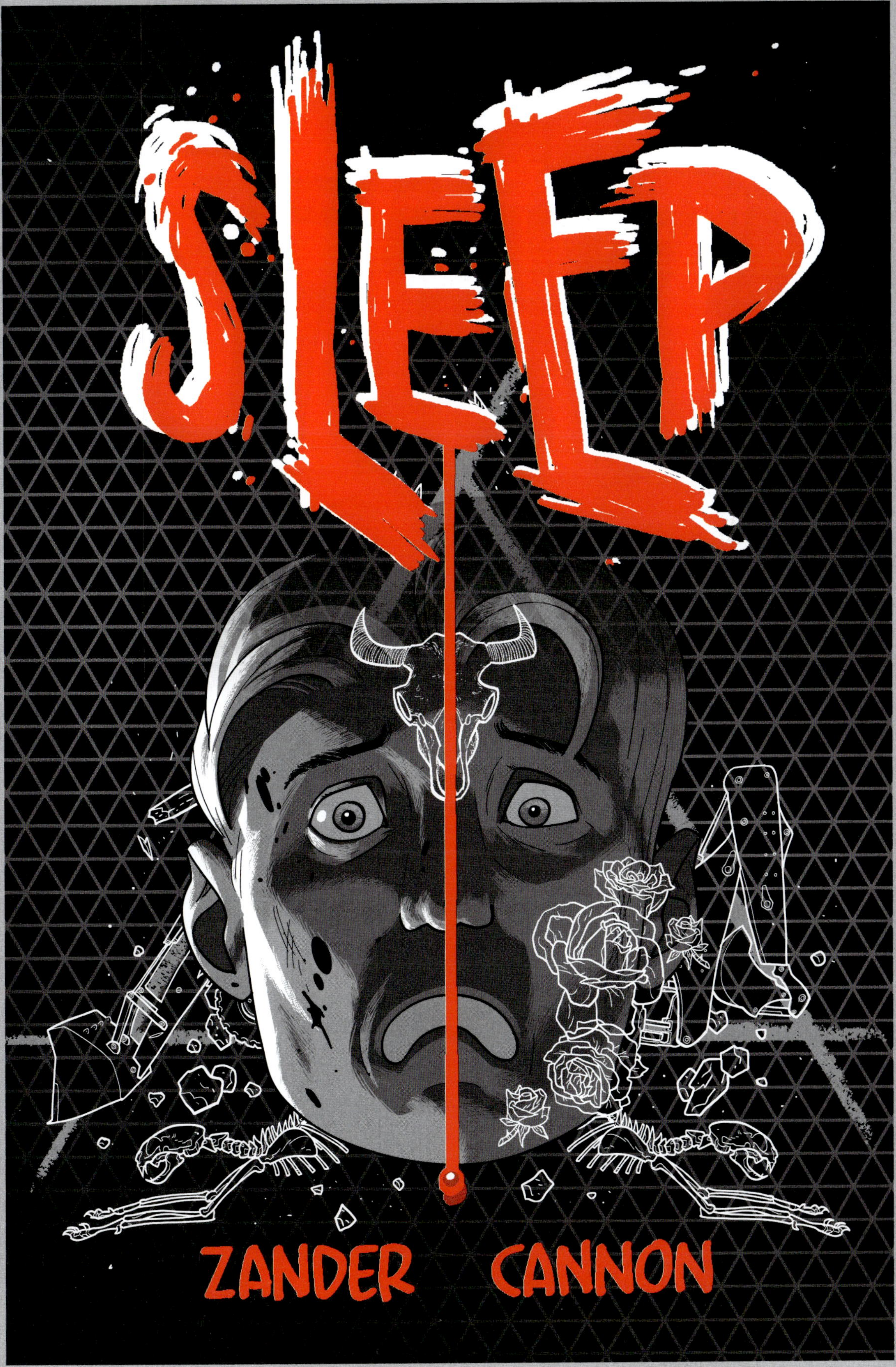

ISSUE 1 COVER BY **ZANDER CANNON**

ISSUE 1 VARIANT COVER BY **RYAN BROWNE**

ISSUE 2 COVER BY **ZANDER CANNON**

ISSUE 2 VARIANT COVER BY **TIM SEELEY**

ISSUE 3 COVER BY **ZANDER CANNON**

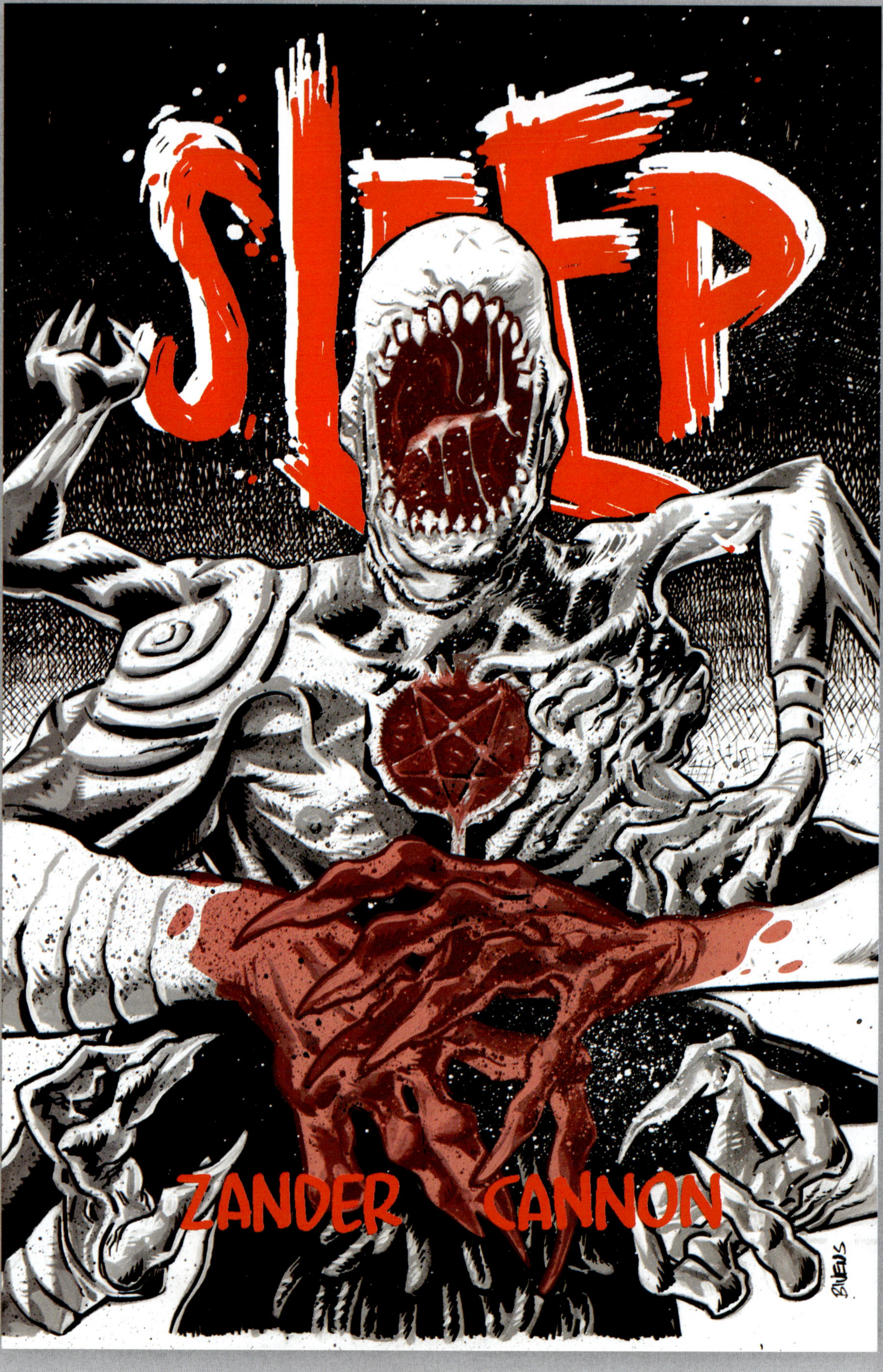

ISSUE 3 VARIANT COVER BY **JOHN BIVENS**

ISSUE 4 COVER BY **ZANDER CANNON**

ISSUE 4 VARIANT COVER BY **MATT KINDT**

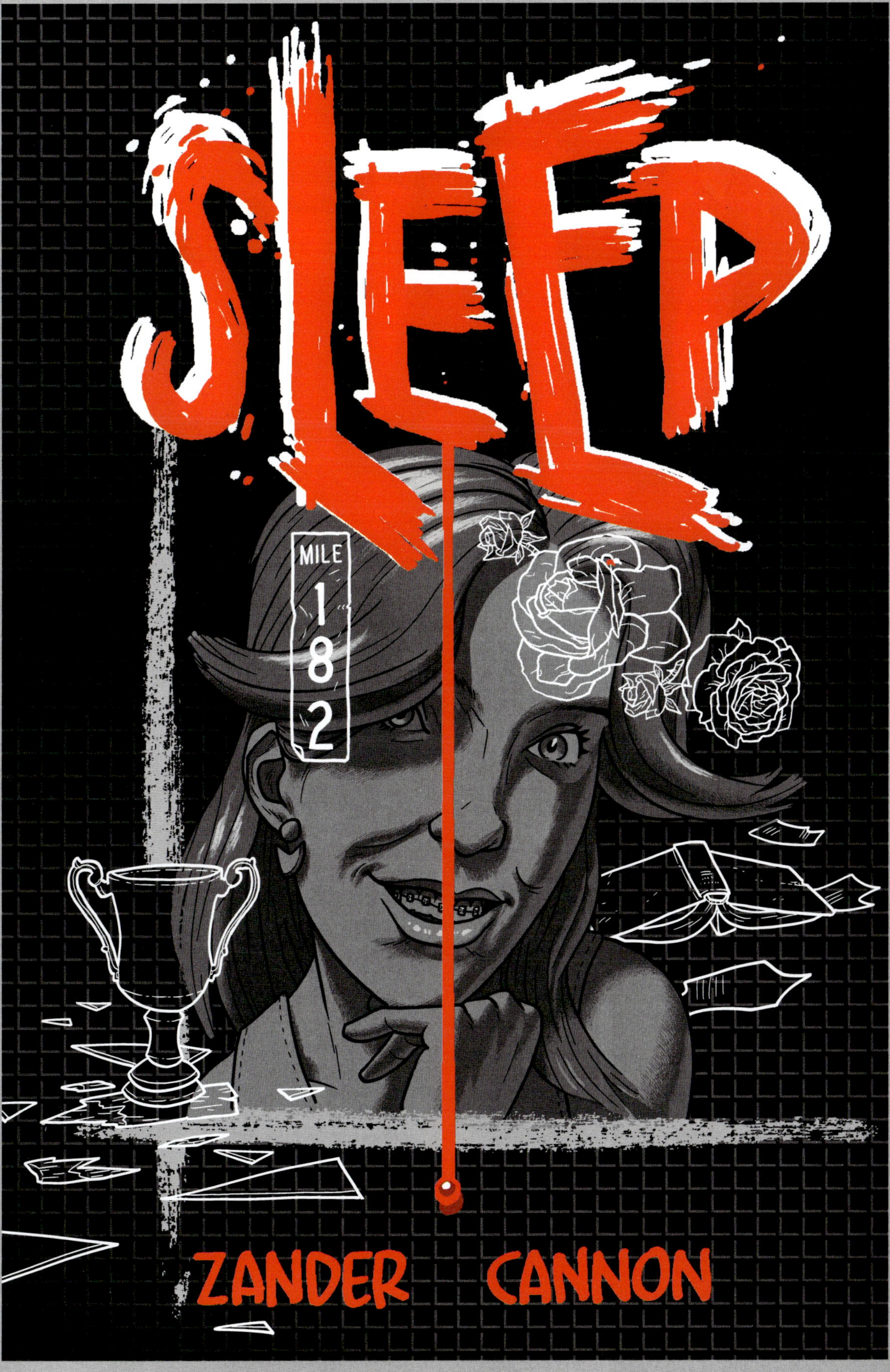

ISSUE 5 COVER BY **ZANDER CANNON**

ISSUE 5 VARIANT COVER BY **BRIAN HURTT**

ISSUE 6 COVER BY **ZANDER CANNON**

ISSUE 6 VARIANT COVER BY **MATT BORS**

ISSUE 7 COVER BY **ZANDER CANNON**

ISSUE 7 VARIANT COVER BY **KEVIN CANNON**

ISSUE 8 COVER BY **ZANDER CANNON**

ISSUE 8 VARIANT COVER BY **GENE HA**